W9-DGX-518

Researching Sociology On The Internet

D.R. Wilson
College of Education & Behavioral Sciences
Houston Baptist University

David L. Carlson
Anthropology Department
Texas A&M University

WADSWORTH

THOMSON LEARNING

Australia • Canada • Mexico • Singapore • Spain • United Kingdom • United States

For more information, contact
Wadsworth/Thomson Learning
10 Davis Drive
Belmont, CA 94002-3098
USA

For more information about our products, contact us: Thomson Learning Academic Resource Center
1-800-423-0563
http://www.wadsworth.com

International Headquarters
Thomson Learning
International Division
290 Harbor Drive, 2nd Floor
Stamford, CT 06902-7477
USA

UK/Europe/Middle East/South Africa
Thomson Learning
Berkshire House
168-173 High Holborn
London WC1V 7AA
United Kingdom

Asia
Thomson Learning
60 Albert Complex, #15-01
Singapore 189969

Canada
Nelson Thomson Learning
1120 Birchmount Road
Toronto, Ontario M1K 5G4
Canada

ISBN 0-534-56894-7

Table of Contents

Preface

This guide is written for students who are generally familiar with the World Wide Web and the Internet, but do not have much experience using the web to study sociology. Part I of the guide provides you with the answers to some simple questions about the Internet and the World Wide Web. Basic tasks such as communicating, searching, and learning are covered in some detail with a focus on how to use the Internet to place the study of sociology into a broader context. Addresses for the web sites mentioned in the text are included at the end of each section. Part II focuses in more detail on parts of the World Wide Web that cover sociology. Research methods, socialization, culture, social groups, families, deviance, inequality, institutions, social dynamics and social change are all discussed. Within each of these fields, students are introduced to specific web sites as starting points for Internet research. In addition, there are sections on applied sociology and careers in sociology.

If you are a student, this guide can help you to prepare for class and complete course assignments. The Internet is not a replacement for using the resources in your school library, but it can help you to find those resources more effectively. It can also help you find material that is not locally available. You can use the Internet to keep up to date on current news reports that cover areas of the world or topics that are covered in your textbook or in class lectures. Accessing this kind of information can help you to be a better student in several ways. You will be able to ask better questions in class and you will remember things better if you link what you are learning in the classroom to what is going on in the world around you. Using the Internet to supplement your study of sociology can be a successful active learning strategy. You will also develop better skills as a critical thinker, because you will find many competing viewpoints on the web. Evaluating these sites will strengthen your ability to interpret arguments and compare contrasting views.

If you are a sociology instructor, you may be looking for ways to incorporate this guide into your course. There are at least eight ways you can use the information in this guide to enhance classroom instruction.

1. **You can provide students with an assigned web site and related critical thinking questions.** This is a good way for students to begin to become comfortable with the web. It can also be a way to more actively engage students in the learning process.

2. **Read a specific document on the web and evaluate it in light of what has been taught in the classroom.** This activity asks students to apply critical judgment to the materials they find on the web. Since you will be providing the web address, it requires little of the student in the way of web-expertise, but helps them develop the evaluation skills that are necessary for becoming a critical thinker.

3. **You can assign students a topic and ask them to search the internet for a web site that provides relevant information.** This activity is more challenging since students must use search engines to locate sites and may have to evaluate the quality of alternate sources. In some cases there may be more than one "correct" answer. Evaluation of this activity should focus on the process of locating and appraising information.

4. **Have students search for specific categories of web sites.** In this instance, students are to synthesize numerous sites and organize them by content. Students will be able to develop organizational skills while using the Internet to learn course content.

5. **Research a current social problem on the web.** Here students can be exposed to a broad range of competing and conflicting ideas related to current social experience. This activity involves more refined skill in searching the web for more specific information and in sifting through numerous possible web sites for those that are most relevant. It also involves a critical evaluation of two or more positions.

6. **Students can use the Internet as a source of news information.** There are a number of major and minor media outlets on the Internet. Students can compare media coverage locally, nationally and globally. Information collected from news sites can be used by students to give brief updates or major presentations on current events. Having students collect current information about social phenomena can be used to connect classroom learning to real world experience.

7. **Require students to use resources from the web in their research papers.** The web should not be the only source of information, but requiring students to search for information on a specific topic will help them develop their search skills and learn how to evaluate and cite material they find on the web.

8. **Studying the culture of the net.** Here the web is not a resource for information; it is an example of virtual culture for the student to investigate. These activities do not focus on facts or competing positions, but instead on how the web creates new opportunities for cultural interaction and how the web contributes to the development of a global culture.

These are just some starting points for researching social phenomena using the Internet. As you and your students become more familiar with the web, you will certainly find other useful sites and even ways to integrate the web into your classes. As you do, I would very much like to hear about them.

D.R. Wilson
Houston Baptist University
drwilson@hbu.edu

PART I.
GUIDE TO USING THE INTERNET

Introduction

You probably already use the Internet. It is mentioned on the news and in newspapers and magazines every day. It is either the greatest boon to modern civilization or the greatest curse. As a student of sociology, you probably have an opinion on this debate. This guide does not attempt to resolve that issue, but it does provide you with basic information concerning what is out there on the Internet and how you find it. Once you know how to locate information, you will be able to find out more about any of the topics discussed here. If you know little about the Internet, this guide is your first step. If you are already an experienced net surfer, this guide may give you some new ideas about how to use the web to enhance your education. The Internet does not render traditional methods of communication and education obsolete; instead it supplements and amplifies them. In order to use the net you will need to develop new skills and refine ones that you already have.

The **Internet** (or just "net") is a "network of networks." It is a standard method by which computers can communicate with one another regardless of whether they are large or small computers and regardless of the operating system they use. It is a kind of universal language for computers. At first the primary use of the net was for electronic mail, transferring files, and operating computers remotely. More recently, additional functions have been added to make it easier to exchange information and ideas over the net. The most important of these is a way of transferring pages of information containing text, multimedia, and links to other pages. These **hypertext** pages are retrieved and displayed by programs called "**browsers**." Collectively, these pages make up the part of the Internet called the "**World Wide Web**" (or just "web"). Although the **Net** refers to the interconnected networks and the **Web** refers to the interlinked hypertext pages, most people do not distinguish between the two consistently. In this guide I will use the terms interchangeably.

A reasonable way of visualizing the Internet is to think of a series of nodes (computers or whole computer networks) that are connected to one another. Each node is connected to only a few other nodes so getting information from one node to another one means that the information travels through many other nodes before reaching its destination. This roundabout approach makes it simpler to add a new node since only a few connections need to be added and it also means that information has many different paths that it could take in getting from one node to another. If one path is broken, the information is just rerouted along another set of paths. The network does not care what kind of information is being moved. It could be an email file, a picture, a sound file, or a video.

The guide is divided into two sections. The first part answers "Frequently Asked Questions" (**FAQs**) about the Internet and the World Wide Web and describes how you can use the net as a student. The addresses of the web sites (the Universal Resource Locators or **URLs**) are listed at the end of each section. The second part of the guide focuses specifically on how to use the net to enhance your understanding of sociology and provides useful information for researching specific topics within content areas such as research methods, socialization, culture, social groups, social control, social inequality, institutions, social dynamics and social change.

Frequently Asked Questions

Where did the Internet come from? The history of the Internet and the World Wide Web is interesting because it developed from a few simple requirements for a robust network. It grew amazingly fast into a global information network linking millions of people and millions of pages together.

What do I need to get on the Net? This short section gives you some pointers to getting started on the web. Since there are differences in computers, software, and methods of connecting to the Net, it may not meet your exact needs, but it should help you to ask knowledgeable questions.

What kinds of information will I find on the Web? This section talks about the different kinds of files on the Web. Some can be viewed directly with your browser software (probably Netscape or Internet Explorer), but others require special programs. The file types and the special programs you may need are summarized here.

Is it safe? News media enjoy running stories on the dangers of the Net. This section provides a brief introduction to potential hazards on the Net including viruses, cookies, java programs, and communicating with strangers.

Is the information on the Net reliable? The simple answer is, "Some of it." This chapter gives you some basic tools to help you develop critical skills. Just as you cannot believe everything people tell you and you cannot believe everything you read in the paper, you cannot believe everything you read or see on the Web.

Where should I start? When you connect to the Net and start your browser, a start page is loaded. This section talks about start pages and **portals**. If you just want to explore the Web, you might try one of the Web Rings that links sites related to sociology or the Virtual Library of Sociology.

Where Did the Internet Come From?

The Internet was born thirty years ago in the midst of the Cold War. With the increasing threat of nuclear destruction, the U.S. military wanted to be able to operate computers remotely and wanted to be able communicate over its computer network even if large parts of it were destroyed. This meant that the network had to be decentralized and it had to be possible to route information dynamically. Out of these requirements ARPANET began in 1969 with four nodes. It grew slowly at first. Nodes were added and at each node additional computers (hosts) were connected. By 1984 there were 1,000 hosts by 1989 there were 100,000 and by 1992 there were 1,000,000. Today there are about 72 million hosts.

One of the important reasons for connecting computers was to allow people to access them remotely. Powerful computers were expensive and it was easier and less expensive to let researchers run programs on those computers remotely. Communication between people at the various nodes to ask for assistance or schedule time on a computer took the form of electronic messages (which were much cheaper than phone calls). As the net grew and the cost of computers dropped, the ability to run programs remotely became less important than the ability to send and receive electronic messages. **Email** quickly became one of the principal uses of the developing networks. As useful as electronic messages are, they are not very flexible if you want to circulate information among a group of people and allow them to discuss a topic. Two approaches to this problem were developed that expanded on the basic idea of email. The first was the **mailing list**, a computer program that would forward the same message to a list of addresses. If you subscribed to the list, you would receive any message that was sent to the list. The lists were not limited to serious topics. One of the first ones was SF-LOVERS for fans of science fiction. The second innovation was **electronic bulletin boards**. You sent your email message to the bulletin board where it remained for a period of time. Anyone who saw it could reply to you directly or could post their own message. The first bulletin board system was USENET, which began operating in 1979. There are separate bulletin boards (called newsgroups) for different topics. True to the decentralized concept of the Internet the USENET bulletin boards are located on many different computers, which communicate with one another to keep their copies of the messages up to date.

Electronic mail and bulletin boards have proven valuable and have spread beyond the Internet. Bulletin board systems based on home computers with modems offered email to local subscribers and in 1983 many of these were linked together into a loose network called FidoNet. FidoNet was based entirely on communication over phone lines. Commercial information systems such as Compuserve, America Online and Prodigy also offered email. Within the last few years virtually all of them have connected to the Internet so that the number of different (and incompatible) email systems is shrinking.

As the net grew, ways of using it expanded as well. One advantage that centralized commercial systems such as America Online had was the ability to allow people to communicate in real time by typing messages that were instantly distributed to others who were logged in. They could also play interactive games against one another in real time. A simple messaging system for sending a message to a single location was present in early versions of the Internet, but allowing several people to send messages at the same time was not really possible until the development of **Internet Relay Chat** in 1988.

Much of the software for the net was developed by people in their spare time and was made freely available for use by anyone else. The problem on the Internet was that you could only get a file if you knew exactly where it was. In 1990 a program called **Archie** was released that allowed people to search archives of hundreds of computers to find a particular program file.

The watershed year for the Internet as we know it today was 1991. A strong method of encrypting information was released (Pretty Good Privacy) which is closely related to the methods used today to encrypt commercial transactions. Encryption scrambles the text of the message so that, even if it is intercepted, it cannot be read. A new way of distributing textual information was introduced by researchers at the University of Minnesota called **Gopher**. Gopher exploded on the net as people began to make various kinds of information available. Since it distributed text only, it was well suited to slow computers and slow Internet connections. Not so well suited at the time was a more complex system that allowed text and graphics files to be distributed and combined into a single page. Developed in Switzerland, it involved a way of formatting a document to contain text, graphics, and most importantly links to other documents. The links could be to documents or images located anywhere on the Internet. Because of this feature, the system was called the World-Wide Web (WWW). The only problem was that many people in 1991 still accessed the Internet via terminals that could not display graphics. Gopher grew rapidly for several years because it was designed around the limitations of existing equipment.

In 1992, the number of hosts on the Internet reached 1,000,000. The following year a graphical browser for the Internet was developed at the University of Illinois called **Mosaic**. The web caught up with and surpassed Gopher in that year. Universities and government agencies moved rapidly to the web. The US White House and the United Nations come online with the US Senate and House following in 1994. That same year the first shopping malls and cyberbanks begin to appear and Pizza Hut sold its first online pizza. To advertise their green card lottery services an Arizona law firm sent an email advertisements to thousands of people thereby introducing **"spam"** (the email equivalent of junk mail) to the net.

Since 1994, the number of web sites has grown dramatically. Several of the people who developed the Mosaic web browser left the University of Illinois to found Netscape, while Microsoft started shipping a web browser with its Windows 95 operating system. Competition between Microsoft and Netscape resulted in browsers absorbing the functions of many separate programs (for example email and newsreaders). Limitations in the original web standards were removed by adding capabilities for multimedia (streaming audio and video, virtual reality modeling) and interactivity (Java and Shockwave programming). Although the capacity of the net has increased steadily, the growth in the number of users and the **bandwidth** (number of bits moved per second) for each user has grown at least as fast.

The Internet is big, but because it is decentralized, we can only make educated guesses about how big. The number of hosts on the net was about 72 million by early 2000. Estimates of how many people are online around the world vary from about 150 to 200 million. The total number of pages on the web has been estimated recently to be about one billion.

What Do I Need to Get on the Net?

You will need four things to begin using the net: a computer (or access to one at your university computer center), a connection to a network, a browser, and a computer account (for email).

You can access the net with almost any **computer** made today. The net is accessible via IBM/Microsoft machines, Apple MacIntosh computers, unix workstations, and large mainframe systems. If you have your own computer, you are set. If you are a student at a university, there are probably computer labs where you can use a computer. Increasingly public libraries are also providing access to the net, so you might be able to access the net there.

Secondly, you need a **connection** to a network that is connected to the net. There are several kinds of connections and new options are being added. Many computers come with a modem that allows them to access a network over a telephone line. Modem connections have the advantage that you can use them to connect to the net wherever there is a phone jack. They have the disadvantage that they are the slowest way to connect. Your university probably provides much faster ethernet connections in computer labs, offices, some classrooms, and even dormitories. Ethernet connections are significantly faster and do not use your telephone line. Other options such as cable modems, satellite systems, and digital subscriber lines are available in parts of the country.

Thirdly, you may need a **browser**. A browser is a software application that allows you to retrieve and display web pages. Most computers come with them already installed. The two dominant programs are Netscape Communicator[1] by Netscape and Internet Explorer[2] by Microsoft. Both browsers have the ability to access email and news groups, although there are dedicated programs for those functions as well that you may find more useful. When you start the browser, it will look much like a word processing program. You will see formatted text and graphics and you will be able to scroll up and down the page. The thing to remember is that the documents

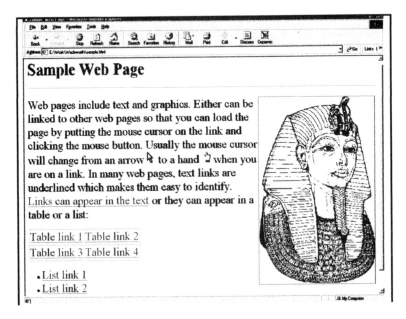

Sample Web Page

Web pages include text and graphics. Either can be linked to other web pages so that you can load the page by putting the mouse cursor on the link and clicking the mouse button. Usually the mouse cursor will change from an arrow ▶ to a hand ☝ when you are on a link. In many web pages, text links are underlined which makes them easy to identify. Links can appear in the text or they can appear in a table or a list:

Table link 1 Table link 2
Table link 3 Table link 4

- List link 1
- List link 2

you view in the browser are not on your computer but somewhere else. On most web pages, underlined text identifies links to other documents. If you click your mouse on some underlined text, your browser will load the page defined by the link. Web pages use a cryptic addressing system called a **universal resource locator** (URL) that specifies a particular domain address and a particular file at that domain. Because the addresses are cumbersome to type (and the browser is very picky about spelling), you should **bookmark** pages you want to return to (check your browser's help files for instructions on how to bookmark a site).

You may discover that you need some additional programs to view some pages. These programs are referred to as **plug-ins** because they work within your browser. For example the Adobe Acrobat® plug-in allows you to view pages that have been specially formatted. Several plug-ins give you the ability to play video and sound files while others let you maneuver within a three dimensional virtual space (VRML). Any of these programs can be downloaded once you are on the net. Sites that have content requiring these programs usually provide a link that you can use to download and install the software.

Finally, you need a computer **account**. Your university computer center probably has information about how to get a student account. You can also get an account with an Internet Service Provider (ISP). The account allows you to log on to the network and provides storage space for email messages that people send you until you retrieve or discard them. Internet providers include national firms such as America Online and AT&T as well as local firms that serve a single region.

What Types of Media Are on the Web?

As originally conceived, web documents consisted of formatted text and images. Soon other kinds of media were added to web pages. First sound and pre-formatted documents, then animations and virtual spaces, and finally video were added. Unfortunately web browsers could not handle these content types directly so **plug-in** programs that could handle the new content types either within the browser window or in a separate window were developed. As new content types were introduced, so too were new formats so that more than one plug-in program is needed for each content type. A new series of plug-ins tries to deal with multiple content types in an effort to reduce the confusion somewhat. Currently on the web you will find all of the following types of media:

HTML **Text**. These are the standard files used on web sites. They are formatted using "Hyper-Text Markup Language" (HTML) which means that the file contains text and codes (markup language) to tell your web browser how to format the text and where to set up links to other documents.

Pre-Formatted Text. In contrast to html documents, pre-formatted documents are not interpreted by the web browser, but are displayed exactly as they are presented without markup codes. In general, browsers will not try to format documents that have a file extension of "txt" which is the most common way of identifying ASCII documents. These documents are displayed in your browser using a fixed pitch font (such as Courier) whereas HTML documents are generally displayed using a variable pitch font (such as Times Roman). ASCII is mostly used for older files that have not been converted to HTML and for programs (where indenting and line breaks help to make the program more legible).

HTML documents do not give you complete control over how your document will look on some else's computer. HTML does not support some common formatting features (notably tabs). Browsers do not always wrap text around images in the same way and the sizing of table rows and columns can differ for different browsers and for different versions of a particular browser. For these reasons you will find some documents on the web that are not written in HTML. These pre-formatted documents use other ways of composing a document. Currently the most common alternate format is Adobe® Acrobat. Acrobat allows you to take a document from a word processing, spreadsheet, or presentation program and preserve all of the original formatting. The only drawback is that the new file cannot be interpreted directly by your browser. Adobe provides Acrobat Reader[3], a free program that can read Acrobat files. The reader will display the Acrobat file in the browser window.

Images. Image files come in several varieties and most web browsers support them without needing any plug-in programs. The most common types on the web include GIF, JPG, and TIFF. Each has some differences that make them more appropriate in certain circumstances. GIF and TIFF files preserve every pixel in the original file (so they are referred to as "lossless"). In most cases they will require larger files than JPG, which preserves most of the information (so they are referred to as "lossy"). Typically you will not notice the difference between the two, except that the JPG image will load much faster. TIFF files are usually used to provide high-resolution images that can be used by news media or for presentations.

Sound. There are many types of audio files on the web. Standard audio files contain a digital encoding of sound. They can be very large, on the order of 20K to 60K per second. For that reason these formats are usually used to record short theme songs, snappy quotations, and sound effects. You will run across three types on the web, each associated with a different computer type: AU (UNIX), AIFF (MacIntosh), and WAV (Windows). Increasingly, the web seems to be standardizing on WAV files.

MIDI files store the instructions for creating a melody or tune. MIDI files are much smaller, but require a sound card in your computer that uses the instructions to create the sounds, much like a player piano plays songs by following coded instructions on a role of paper. The drawback of MIDI files is that they will sound somewhat different depending on the software and hardware that is used to play them.

Recently, a method has been developed of compressing sound files by discarding some of the details so that the files are smaller and the download times are shorter. These compressed audio files are called MP3 and are used extensively to record music. There are whole web sites devoted to programs that are used to play these files and to listings of music that has been encoded. Microsoft's Windows Media Player[4] and Real Network's RealJukebox[5] can play these files.

The sound files just mentioned all have to be downloaded to your computer's hard drive before they can be played. This means that they cannot be used for live sound such as that of a radio broadcast. Streaming audio files, in contrast, begin playing as soon as part of the file has arrived. This feature makes it possible to send live broadcasts over the web, and allows you to listen to longer programs. The dominant format for streaming audio is RealAudio. It is supported by the RealPlayer[6] by Real Networks. The Windows Media Player by Microsoft also supports the RealAudio format.

Virtual Spaces. Virtual spaces create a world that you can explore by using a set of controls on the bottom and sides of your browser window. You can view the world from any angle, up close or far away. They are still in the formative stages. They usually involve large files and your movement through the world may not be smooth unless the world is simple and your computer has lots of memory and a fast processor. You will need a plug-in program to experience virtual spaces and there are several for each of the major browsers. A number of virtual worlds that recreate archaeological sites and great architectural structures are available on the web.

Video. As with sound, the first file formats for video compress the images into a single, very large file. There are three major formats: MOV (Apple QuickTime[7]), AVI (Microsoft Audio Visual), and MPEG. The biggest drawback to these formats is that you have to wait for the entire file to download so live broadcasts are not feasible and the amount of video you can download is limited by your available hard disk space.

Streaming video works like streaming audio. You begin watching the video while it is downloading. The entire file is not stored on your computer, so you are not limited by your available hard disk space. The major plug-ins for viewing video are RealPlayer by RealNetworks and the Windows Media Player by Microsoft.

Program Files. These are binary files containing machine language instructions designed to work on your computer. Web browsers will usually ask if you want to run the program directly or save it on your hard drive. Usually you will save the program and then run it to install the program. Download these programs only from reliable sources to avoid the possibility of getting one that contains a virus.

Is It Safe?

As long as you take sensible precautions, the net is safe. Growing up in contemporary society, we are accustomed to interacting with strangers in public settings. Since we access the net from the privacy of our homes or offices, it is easy to forget that the net is a public place. Information on the net does not travel directly from your computer to the computer you are contacting. It travels a circuitous route through many other computers. Each step along the route involves making a copy of your information, sending it to the next computer along the way, and then deleting the copy. Unless the information is encrypted, someone else can view it. Online vendors now generally encrypt all sensitive information (such as name, address, credit card number) and web browsers use an icon (usually some kind of padlock) to let you know that the information is being encrypted. On the other hand, it is rare for email messages to be encrypted. Unless you are encrypting your message, don't include information that you don't want others to see.

Another security concern involves information that you provide to a company or vendor when you register at their web site, which means providing your name, email address, and possibly other information. Usually registration involves storing some information on your computer (a file called a cookie). Web pages use cookies to recognize when you return to their site. This allows them to customize their pages according to your interests (and to try to pick advertising that you would be more likely to find interesting). Cookie files are also needed when you customize a web page (for example,

9

you set up a special version of Yahoo! called My Yahoo!). When you are at a shopping site, cookies are used to keep track of your selections until you complete your purchase. You can set your browser to notify you when a web page tries to store information on your computer, and you can set your browser to refuse all cookie files.

Your name and email address are probably already available on the web unless you have had your account for a short time. Your university may include some information about you in a publicly accessible directory unless you specifically request that they not do so. You should be very careful with your social security number or credit card numbers. Before providing any information, make sure that the web site indicates how it will use the information. There are currently no U.S. laws protecting your privacy when you provide information to a web site. Legislation may be proposed in the future and the European Union has put strong restrictions in place that may eventually become a model for the U.S.

A third area of concern involves computer viruses and other attacks on your computer as a result of your connection to the net. Again, taking reasonable precautions will protect you or will minimize the damage if your computer is infected. The most important precaution (and the one you are most likely to ignore) is to keep up-to-date backup copies of important files on your computers. You do not need to backup software programs since you have the original distribution disks, but you should backup text, graphics, and spreadsheet files that you have created. Computers are very reliable, but they all fail eventually. If you lose valuable information or work, it will be no consolation to know that a hard disk crash rather than a virus caused it.

A computer virus is a small program that copies itself to the hard disk on your computer (and often to any floppy disk inserted in the computer). It typically hides itself by attaching to programs already present on your hard drive, particularly the system files that load whenever you turn your computer on. Some viruses simply put silly messages on your screen, others slow your computer down, and others deliberately damage or erase files. Software that detects viruses is readily available and should help you to avoid infection. Since a virus is a program, you generally cannot be infected from a text, graphic, or spreadsheet file. As computer software has become more complex, it has become possible to embed macro commands (small simple programs) into these files. Software manufacturers have taken steps to prevent these macro commands from being used to insert viruses, but no one can guarantee the continued effectiveness of these measures.

Your computer can be a target for hackers if you are linked through an ethernet connection or a cable modem and you leave your computer turned on. Make certain that you have set the security features in your operating system to restrict access to your disk drives. If you want others to be able to access files on your computer (such as your web pages), put them in a subdirectory and restrict access to that subdirectory.

You will meet people on the net via email, electronic conferences, chat rooms, via web pages, or through personal ads that people place on the net (just like those found in newspapers). Remember that you do not have many of the cues that you subconsciously use to size people up. They control every statement that they make to you ("slips of the tongue" are much less likely) and they control how much or little you know about them (via their web page or the fact that you do not have acquaintances in common). They even control every aspect of their appearance since they can send you a copy of anyone's picture. You cannot be overly cautious in these situations and no one who is being honest with you would expect you to do otherwise. Be careful about divulging personal information about yourself. If you do decide to meet someone in person that you have met on the net, take a good friend along and meet only during the day in a busy, public setting.

Is the Information on the Net Reliable?

The quality of the information on the net varies just as it does everywhere else. The constitutional protections of freedom of the press and freedom of speech are not restricted to truthful or accurate statements. You should assume that anyone can say or write anything on the web. Offensive and sexually explicit material does exist on the net. If you wish to block your access to such material, programs exist that will prevent your browser from retrieving pages from known sources of such material. Since we do not all agree on what is offensive, these programs may require some fine-tuning on your part.

While we each recognize pretty quickly what offends us, we do not as readily recognize misleading or false information. In order to use the net effectively you must develop your critical facilities so that you can distinguish reliable from misleading information. The late Carl Sagan referred to this skill as "The Fine Art of Baloney Detection." It takes practice and as you might guess there are web pages that will help you learn about how to evaluate web pages (for example Internet Detective[8]). Other good pages are Critical Thinking Resources[9] at Longview Community College and A Student's Guide to WWW Research: Web Searching, Web Page Evaluation, and Research Strategies[10] by Craig Branham.

Four characteristics are usually cited as important in evaluating print journalism. They apply equally well to web pages. They include the **source** of the information, the **objectivity** of the author, the **logic** of the argument, and **independent sources** of support for the argument or claim.

Welcome to Internet
Detective

an interactive tutorial
on evaluating the quality of Internet

The **source** of the information includes the author and the publisher of the web page or pages. In some cases they will be the same person. The fact that someone is an expert on a particular topic does not mean they are always correct, but it does indicate that they have spent considerable time studying and researching the topic. They are likely to have considered many alternative explanations and are likely to make appropriate judgments regarding relevant versus irrelevant facts. Authority is limited, however. A world-recognized authority on particle physics is not necessarily an authority on anything else. In print journalism, an important role of the publisher is to provide fact-checking and independent verification of the claims made by authors. In professional journals, other authorities review articles before they are published. However, on the net, it is not always easy to determine if there has been any independent evaluation of information. News organizations who depend on their reputations for accurate reporting are likely to have conducted some level of review on the material distributed on their web sites and some technical journals use peer reviews for articles published on the web. In most other cases, the fact that an organization hosts a web page should not be considered as evidence that the material on the page has been reviewed or verified by anyone. In some cases it may be difficult to determine the author of a web page. If there is no information about the author, you should be more skeptical of the accuracy of the material.

Another clue to the reliability of information is the **objectivity** of the author. There are very few topics about which everyone in the world agrees. Look to see if the author is attempting to be objective and present both sides of the issue or is advocating one side. Some web pages are clearly intended to advocate a particular viewpoint with no effort to consider other sides of an issue. Such pages can be a source of information for the point of view presented, but should not be used as a source of information for other points of view (find other web pages advocating those points of view). Watch out for a tendency in advocacy pages to dismiss counter arguments or to demean people who do not hold the view being presented.

You should also examine the **logic** of the arguments presented by the author. Ask yourself if the argument makes sense. Can you see simple alternative explanations that have been ignored or overlooked? Make certain that the arguments are complete enough for you to see how each step leads to the next one. Watch out for over-generalization where the author convinces you that a claim holds in one case, therefore it must be universally true. Also watch out for "burden of proof" tricks where the author tries to shift the burden of proof to the other side (e.g. "although many claims of visitation by extraterrestrials have been proven false, how could they all be false?"). Other tricks involve dismissing opposing viewpoints by questioning their proponents' motives (*ad hominem* attacks) or criticizing an extreme version of an opposing viewpoint that no one would support (straw man arguments).

Statistics also provide opportunities to mislead. There are several common techniques for misdirection. One involves using raw counts rather than rates. For example, "evidence of our more violent society is provided by the fact that the number of homicides increased 50% from 1970 to 1990." Of course population increased as well. There was an increase in homicide rates, but it was about 20% not 50%. A second trick involves ignoring control groups, "in a large sample, 18% of the people who ate olestra (a fat substitute) complained of some form of stomach distress the following day." True, but almost 20% of the control group who did not eat olestra also complained of stomach distress. Finally, watch out for confusion of correlation with causation. Just because two variables increase over time, it does not follow that one causes the other. They could both be caused by a third factor that was not measured in the study. For example population growth ("The need for gun control is demonstrated by the fact that the number of homicides committed in a city is directly correlated with the number of guns sold.").

Finally, you should consider **independent sources** of information that support or fail to support the claims made on the page. Are you are aware of opposing views or information that are not mentioned on the web page? If so, you should be skeptical of the author's authority and doubt his or her objectivity. Check to see if the author provides references for factual claims or arguments. Search the web to look for other web pages that would support or contradict the claims made by the author. You should consider the evaluation of information to be a process not an event. As you find out more and more about a topic, use your new information to reevaluate materials you encountered earlier.

Where Should I Start?

When you start your web browser, a hypertext page loads automatically. That page is your **start page**. The default start page is usually located at the web site of the company that produced the web browser. You can change the start page at any time by changing the site listed in your preferences. You can create a small web page of your own and load it from your own computer. It can be little more than a list or a table containing the pages you most often like to visit. Alternatively you can customize the default start page or specify that another site will be your start page. **Web portal** sites provide a wide variety of information in a compact format including news, stock quotes, a search engine, a subject classification of the web and more. You customize the page to include particular kinds of news (e.g. only sports), particular stocks, your favorite web pages, and more. You may also be able to chat with other people who are currently online, set up an email account, or even a web page at your portal site. MyYahoo![11] By Yahoo!, Netcenter[12] by Netscape, and MSN[13] by Microsoft are examples.

Topical Guides. Most subjects have guides to the web. A great starting point for sociological searches is a site created by Dr. Michael Kearl at Trinity University named A Sociological Tour Through Cyberspace[14]. Other useful guides include: The SocioWeb[15] created and maintained by Mark Blair of Pacific Web, the World Wide Web Virtual Library: Sociology[16], maintained by Dr. Carl Cuneo, Department of Sociology, McMaster University, Hamilton, Ontario, Canada or the University of California at San Diego's site at Data on the Net[17]. At About.com[18] guides review interesting web sites and give suggestions. The Sociology[19] guide is Kathy S. Stolley. **Virtual Society** is Wadsworths online sociology site. It provides information and links related to sociology, the web, and Wadsworth texts. You can find it at Virtual Society: The Wadsworth Sociology Resource Center[20].

Web Rings. A good way to begin browsing the web if you don't have a clear idea of what you want to find is to use a web ring. Web rings are collections of related web sites. Each site in the web ring has a link to the site before it and the site after it in the list. Often the site also has a way to randomly select a site from the web ring. The main web site for web rings is Welcome to WebRing![21] Here you will find information about web rings and how to create them. You will also find subject classifications for the existing web rings and a search function that will let you search for web rings that have a particular word or phrase in their title or description. Below are several web rings that relate to sociology. Adding a site to a web ring is completely voluntary and you may find sites that do not really seem to fit, but this is a good way to begin to surf the net.

1. Sociology Forum Web Ring[22] (10 sites) is a collection of Sociology Web Pages on the Internet.
2. The Sociology Ring[23] (259 sites) The Sociology Ring was started in order to connect the growing number of web sites dealing with the profession. Academic and clinical sociologists, sociology students (graduate or undergraduate), and others are welcome to join the ring.
3. Worldwide Sociology Web Ring[24] (7 sites) This webring is offered to sociology professors and students as a location to link their homepages to others interested in Sociology and those just interested in seeing what other people are doing in Sociology.
4. Everything Postmodern Web Ring[25] (28 sites) The Everything Postmodern web ring is broad collection of pages related to postmodernism and postmodern theory. We are mainly focused on the philosophical and sociological aspects of this genre.
5. Cyberstudies Web Ring[26] (40 sites) The purpose of this webring is to link together sites that have a common interest, which is the STUDY of cyberculture (or electronic culture or Internet culture). The sites in this ring reflect a variety of disciplines, such as cybersociology, cyberanthropology, and psychology.

Web Links

1. Netscape Communicator: http://homenetscape.com/browser/index.html

2. Internet Explorer: http://wwwmicrosof.com/windows/ie/

3. Acrobat Reader: http://adobe.com/prodindex/acrobat/readstep.html

4. Windows Media Player:
   http://www.microsoft.com/windows/mediaplayer/default.asp

5. RealJukebox: http://www.real.com/product/realjukebox/

6. RealPlayer: http://www.real.com/products/player

7. Quick Time: http://www.apple.com/quicktime/

8. Internet Detective: http://sosig.ac.uk/desire/internet-detective.html

9. Critical Thinking Resources:
   http://www.kcmetro.cc.mo.us/longview/ctac/toc.htm

10. A Student's Guide to WWW Research: Web Searching, Web Page EvaluationMSN.COM: http://home.microsoft.com/

11. Yahoo!: http://www.yahoo.com/

12. Netcenter: http://www.home.netscape.com/

13. The Sociological Tour Through Cyberspace
    http://www.trinity.edu/mkearl/index.html

14. The SocioWeb
    http://www.socioweb.com/~markbl/socioweb/

15. World Wide Web Virtual Library: Sociology
    http://www.mcmaster.ca/socscidocs/w3virtsoclib/index.htm

16. Data on the Net: http://odwin.ucsd.edu/idata/

17. About.com: http://www.about.com/

18. Sociology: http://sociology.about.com/science/sociology/mbody.htm

19. Virtual Society:The Wadsworth Sociology Resource Center
    http://sociology.wadsworth.com/

20. Welcome to WebRing!: http://www.webring.com/

21. Sociology Forum Web Ring:
    http://nav.webring.yahoo.com/hub?ring=socforum&list

22. The Sociology Ring:
    http://nav.webring.yahoo.com/hub?ring=sociology&list

23. World Wide Sociology Web Ring:
    http://nav.webring.yahoo.com/hub?ring=wwsociology&list

24. Everything Postmodern Web Ring:
    http://nav.webring.yahoo.com/hub?ring=epostmodern&list

25. Cyberstudies Web Ring:
    http://nav.webring.yahoo.com/hub?ring=cyberstudies&lis

Communicating

Email

Electronic mail and variations of it are the most heavily used aspect of the net. Like regular mail, your message travels to the person you have sent it to and waits to be retrieved and read. It has most of the advantages of regular mail, but it arrives at its destination much faster. One disadvantage of email is that you do not receive any confirmation that the message was read and many people still don't read their email regularly. If you receive a message from someone that you do not communicate with regularly, it doesn't hurt to respond with a simple note that you received the message.

When you get a computer account, you will also get an email address. It will be something like "jsmith@bigu.edu." The part of your email address to the left of the "@" sign is your account name while the part on the right is the **domain name**. The domain name is used to route messages to a particular computer that saves the message in a directory associated with a particular account. The message stays in the directory until you retrieve, read, or delete it. There are two basic ways of handling email accounts. One involves using email software on your personal computer to retrieve all of the new messages from your mail account. You can then read, save, reply, or do whatever you want with each message. Generally the messages are deleted from the computer that stores the messages until you retrieve them. This is convenient if you want to store messages without worrying about using up the space allotted for your email account. The second way is to leave messages on your email account until you delete them. This is convenient if you access your email from different computers (at your campus computer lab or while traveling). You should remember that your messages occupy space on the computer that holds your email account and you have probably been allocated only a certain amount of space. If you receive many messages or a few big messages (with large files attached), your space allocation will fill up and any further messages will be returned to the sender. You may not receive any message when this occurs. For this reason, download your email regularly (method one) or check your email regularly and delete messages you no longer need (method two).

In order to send a message to someone, you need to know their email address. While you can often find it by using some of the search engines on the web, it is usually easiest to ask for the address or have the person send you a message. If you attend a university, there will probably be a phonebook of email addresses on the university web page. When you send a message, include information on the subject line that will let the recipient know what the message is about. Due to spam and the possibility of receiving a virus by email, increasingly people are deleting messages without reading them if they come from strangers or have blank or suspicious subject lines. Most email programs also allow you to add a signature to the bottom of your email message. The signature can provide additional information about you such as your name, phone number, occupation, or web page. You can also delete the signature when you are replying to a message or sending mail to someone you know.

Electronic mail introduces old problems in a new guise, such as, spam or electronic junk mail. People are still learning how to communicate by electronic mail. Many of the non-verbal cues that we use to evaluate what someone is saying are missing: the smile or wink that indicates a remark is intended to be humorous or sarcastic; the hesitation or stress in someone's voice that suggests a reply that might not be completely truthful; the flow of someone's handwriting as a clue to his or her emotional state. In addition, we lose the cues that tell us about the impact of our own words: the frown or scowl that indicates that our words have been interpreted as a threat or insult. Finally, electronic mail makes it easy to communicate with complete strangers who don't know anything about you (such as your sense of humor). Messages that depend on nonverbal qualities are often misunderstood in electronic communication. Sarcasm usually fails. It is easy to respond without thinking, and impossible to take the message back after it has been sent. A second element of electronic communication is that we have not yet developed effective filters for the flow of information. We are accustomed to filtering (ignoring) irrelevant information from television and radio, junk mail, and people around us without giving it much thought. Irrelevant electronic mail messages seem to provoke more hostility than irrelevant information from sources with which we are more accustomed. The best thing about irrelevant email is that simply simply deleting the message easily recycles lost disk space.

Because you respond to someone without seeing them (and they do not see you when they respond) it is easier to ignore simple courtesies and respond in an insulting or offensive manner. Read messages you have composed from beginning to end, before you send them. If you receive an insulting message, delete it and resist the temptation to reply with equal venom. You will not teach the other person a lesson and you will simply make yourself a target for further insults. Develop the ability to shrug off minor insults without dwelling on them. It will serve you well later in life. Remember that the net is decentralized and chaotic. For more helpful hints on email Netiquette visit the <u>Netiquette Home Page</u>[1].

If you receive threatening messages, do not delete them. Save them and forward copies to the system administrators (sysop) of the domain from which the threatening messages are coming. The domain is the part of the email address to the right of the "@" site. There is no standard email address for systems operators so you may have to try several ("sysop@Site.com" or "postmaster@" or "security@" or "abuse@"). Do not delete the message as your copy may contain additional information that your email software did not include in the forwarded copy. Also contact the sysop of you Internet provider or university computer center to get their advice and assistance on how to proceed.

Mailing Lists

Mailing lists make it easy to participate in a discussion with many other people. When you subscribe to a mailing list, you are asking to receive a copy of every message sent to the list. The messages will arrive as email. There are mailing lists covering nearly every conceivable topic. <u>Lizst</u>[2] maintains an index to 90,000 mailing lists where you can search for ones of interest to you.

There are several kinds of lists. Some are restricted and some are not. Restricted lists require the permission of the listowner to subscribe. These lists are used for groups of people who are collaborating on some project and wish to restrict the use of the list very narrowly. For example, your instructor may create a mailing list for a course you are taking and subscription to the list would be limited to those in the class. Lists can also be moderated or unmoderated. In a moderated list, the listowner reviews posts before they are distributed. Moderated lists provide a further check on messages before they are distributed so that only messages on the list topic are distributed. Unmoderated lists allow subscribers to post directly to the list. This speeds up the discussion, but it may result in a higher number of off-topic messages.

If you are new to email, subscribing to a list is a good way to begin receiving email. Some lists generate many messages 50-100 day while other lists generate many fewer messages. A general rule of thumb is that the more general the topic, the more messages per day and the more subscribers, the more messages per day. If you subscribe to a busy list you should check your email daily since once the disk space assigned to your account fills, every message will be returned to the sender or to the listowner (or both). If this happens, you may be removed from the list. You can subscribe again once you have cleared your mailbox. Once you have found a list that you are interested in, you will need to learn how to subscribe. Most of the mailing lists are managed by one of three computer programs: listproc, listserv, or majordomo. Completely in accord with the chaos that is the net, they use somewhat different methods of subscribing and unsubscribing:

LISTPROC

1. To subscribe send an email message to listproc@DomainName containing the message

    SUBSCRIBE ListName YourFirstName YourLastName

2. To leave the list send an email message to listproc@DomainName containing the message

    UNSUBSCRIBE ListName

3. To get information about other commands send an email message to listproc@DomainName containing the message

    HELP

LISTSERV

1. To subscribe send an email message to listserv@Domain containing the message

    SUB ListName YourFirstName YourLastName
2. To leave the list send an email message to listserv@Domain containing the message

    SIGNOFF ListName

3. To get further details send an email message to listserv@Domain containing the message

    HELP

MAJORDOMO

1. To subscribe send an email message to majordomo@Domain containing the message

   SUBSCRIBE ListName

2. To leave the list send an email message to majordomo@Domain containing the message

   UNSUBSCRIBE ListName

3. To get further details send an email message to majordomo@Domain containing the message

   HELP

To subscribe to a list you need to know the list email address and what kind it is. If the list called NEWBIE@BigTimeUniversity.edu is a listserv list, you would send the following message:

   sub NEWBIE YourFirstName YourLastName

to listserv@BigTimeUniversity.edu.

There are some web pages that allow you to subscribe to a list from the web. Follow the instructions and you will be added to the list. The program will send you a standard welcome message with instructions about the list and the list software. Keep this message since you will probably want to refer to it later (and it tells you how to unsubscribe from the list).

Your fellow subscribers on the list make up a limited community. They are not your friends (maybe eventually, but not automatically) and they are not a resource at your beck and call. List communities generally consist of a core of long-term subscribers and others who have recently joined the list. You can avoid the classic "newbie" mistakes by heeding ten simple rules:

1. Know to whom you are replying. Pay close attention to the "To:" field on the email messages you are composing. Some lists are configured so that when you use the "Reply" function, the message goes to the entire list while others set the "Reply" function so that the message goes only to the person who sent the message. There are good reasons for each method, but it is easy to get them confused. Once you have learned the software, you will know how to send messages to the whole list if the default is to the sender and vice versa.

2. The list subscribers are not a replacement for the library. Do not ask for help with your homework or research paper unless you have exhausted the available resources first. Then ask very specific questions, not "Can anyone tell me about the Moundbuilders?"

3. Do not posttest messages or "Hi" messages to the list. Send test messages to your friends or to yourself (your email program will not object if you send a message to yourself). Especially on a large list, many subscribers come and go all the time.

4. Do not quote someone's message, add "I agree" or "I disagree," and then post it back to the list. The list is for discussion, not for voting. The general rule of thumb is that your contribution should be longer than the part of the message you quote.

5. Never, Ever, Ever send your list commands to the mailing list. More sophisticated programs will simply return them to you (often with cryptic error messages), but if it gets through, all of the list subscribers will see that you don't know what you are doing. On top of that, the mailing list program does not monitor the list for commands so it will never see your command.

6. Don't play Paul Revere. There are many pseudo virus alerts that circulate around the net. The "Good Times" virus hoax is the most famous, but there are many others. They circulate on a six to twelve month cycle so once you've been on the net for a year you will have run across most of them. If someone sends you an alert, check it out on the web first (e.g. Symantech's Anti Virus Reference Center[3] or the U.S. Department of Energy Computer Incident Advisory Capability [4]). Both list real viruses and hoaxes.

7. Do not post humorous jokes, stories, or riddles to the mailing list unless that is the topic of the list. Just like the virus hoaxes, most of these have been around for a long time. Also recognize that you are communicating with many different people all over the world and there is a good chance that not only is your story off-topic, it may also be offensive to someone. In sociology the story about the hominid fossil that turns out to be a Barbie doll has been around long enough that it has its own web pages (see if you can find them). For other tired stories visit the Urban Legends Archive[5] or the Urban Legends Reference Page[6].

8. Stay out of flame wars. A flame is an antagonistic or insulting reply. On mailing lists you will meet some of the nicest people in the world. People who will go out of their way to help you with a problem or help you work out the details of an argument you are trying to develop. They will help you even though it is not their job and they will receive no compensation or credit for doing it. You will also find people who are not so generous. People who like to post outrageous statements just in order to see who will take the bait. Don't take the bait and don't respond. It is very unlikely that the person who sent the message is naive or will respond to gentle criticism (or any criticism for that matter).

9. Don't publicly point out people's mistakes. You will make plenty as you are getting started on the net, and you will appreciate people who send you a message privately rather than posting it to the entire list.

10. Finally, when it doubt, just observe. When you first join a list that has been established for a long time, spend a few weeks or a month getting an idea of the ebb and flow of topics and how the subscribers interact. If you have a

question, try to locate an archive for the list (a searchable database of previous posts) to see if it has already been answered.

Distribution lists are one-way mailing lists. You generally subscribe via a form on the web page of the organization that is managing the list. You cannot post to a distribution list, it is just a channel for the organization to send you information, offers, special sale notices, breaking news events, etc. As you are visiting web pages you will run across many opportunities to subscribe to distribution lists. Subscribe to those you want, but if you subscribe to too many you will find your mailbox full, sometimes with material that looks very similar to junk mail. Some distribution lists send messages only every once in a while, while others (especially news agencies) send messages every day. The message usually contains instructions for removing your address from the list.

Newsgroups

Newsgroups are similar to bulletin boards. The original USENET newsgroups were developed early in the history of the Internet and were expanded and reorganized in 1986 ("The Great Renaming"). You do not actually subscribe to a newsgroup, although that fact is often unclear because the software for reading and posting to newsgroups has commands for "subscribing." Actually, "monitoring" would be a better term. The messages on a bulletin board stay on the computer systems of your university or ISP until you retrieve them. When you use your software to "subscribe" to a newsgroup, you are only telling the software to check that group for new messages. You can download all of the new messages in a group or just retrieve the subject lines from the messages to see if any are interesting enough to retrieve. To unsubscribe, you simply tell your software to stop downloading the messages from that group. Newsgroups do not have owners or moderators (except in a few cases) and no one knows when you subscribe or unsubscribe. Newsgroups are a good way to monitor subjects that you are generally interested in, but do not want to receive every message every person sends. Since you do not actually receive the messages, you have to visit the group regularly as messages last only a day or a week depending on how much traffic there is on the group. You may be able to find missed messages at DejaNews[7] where many newsgroups are archived.

Newsgroups are organized around a loose hierarchy. Groups that begin with "comp." are about computers, networks, and software. Groups that begin with "rec." are about recreational activities, "sci." groups cover science, "soc." groups are about social groups and society, "talk." groups are for wide ranging discussion and debate about topics that often trigger passionate responses. Groups beginning with "alt." (Alternate) overlap with the other groups. The group started out as a renegade hierarchy for topics that were originally banned from usenet. Sexually explicit groups are present in the "alt." hierarchy, but so are groups on many other topics. In addition to usenet, there are also newsgroups maintained by major software companies. These newsgroups provide a means for people to ask for assistance and to make suggestions about new features or new products.

There are over 50,000 newsgroups archived at DejaNews, but there are also regional and local groups bringing the total even higher. However, you really only need to know about the groups that are available from your ISP or university. Most will offer access to some newsgroups, but do not offer access to all of them. Maintaining storage space and access for newsgroups is costly so ISPs and universities limit access to their local users. Once you have configured your software to connect to the newsgroup server (if your university is myu.edu, the newsgroup server will often be news.myu.edu), you can retrieve the list of newsgroups carried by your system. Once you have the list, you can select the ones you want to "subscribe" to, but recall that the subscription is only a way of telling your software to check for new messages to that group whenever you check for new newsgroup messages.

Chat and Instant Messaging

In 1988 the ability to link several people together so that they could simultaneously send messages to one another instantaneously (**chat**) was devised. Commercial network services such as Compuserve and America Online already had this capability. Internet Relay Chat (IRC) has expanded in size and flexibility and, to some degree, has been captured by the web. IRC is like a conference call except that everyone has to type what they want to say. Since you need to type quickly to keep up, people use a great variety of acronyms to express things compactly (for example, imho -"in my humble opinion" and rotfl "rolling on the floor laughing"). There are now two ways to chat. The first is through an IRC server that handles hundreds of separate chat rooms (or channels). In order to contact them you need IRC client software (for example Microsoft Chat, available free from Microsoft). After you log into a server, you select the room you want to enter. The second way is through a web site that offers chat capabilities inside your web browser. For these you may not need any additional software or the site may download a program that will work inside your browser to handle the chat features. Yahoo! Chat[8] and MSNBC Chat[9] are two examples. You will have to register before you will be able to chat by providing a handle or alias (the name you want to be known by in the chat room) and your email address.

Most chats are simply collections of people who have come together to discuss a particular topic. There is no moderator and no way to keep the discussion on a particular topic. If you find yourself in a room with someone who makes you uncomfortable, just exit the room. Other chat rooms have moderators who keep the discussion on topic and can disconnect people who are offensive or obscene. Finally, some chats are organized around a celebrity guest. In these chats, you will probably need to submit your question to a moderator to get it passed on to the celebrity guest. Your instructor may use chat sessions to allow people to discuss a topic outside class or to allow you to chat with sociology students in another class (or university). Before getting started you should look at Internet Relay Chat (IRC) Help[10] and Chat Etiquette/Chat Protocol[11].

The latest development in chat is **instant messaging** or paging. Instant messaging allows you to send a message to another person who is online as long as that person is running compatible software. The message generally arrives more quickly than email and the software will tell you if the other person is online. The concept was first popularized by a program called ICQ[12] ("I seek you"). AOL Instant Messenger[13] (America Online) is one of the most popular and is freely available to anyone. Ask your sociology instructor if he or she uses instant messaging. It can be a quick way to get an answer to a question while studying for an exam.

Web Links

1. Netiquette Home Page: http://www.fau.edu/netiquette/netiquette.html

2. Lizst: http://www.liszt.com

3. Symantech's Anti Virus Reference Center: http://www.symantec.com/avcenter/index.html

4. Computer Incident Advisory Capability: http://ciac.llnl.gov/ciac/CIACHome.html

5. Urban Legends Archive: http://www.urbanlegends.com/

6. Urban Legends Reference Page: http://www.snopes.com/

7. DejaNews: http://www.deja.com/usenet/

8. Yahoo! Chat: http://chat.yahoo.com/

9. MSNBC Chat: http://www.msnbc.com/chat/default.asp

10. Internet Relay Chat (IRC) Help: http://www.irchelp.org/

11. Chat Etiquette/Chat Protocol: http://www.minopher.net.au/WebEd/protocol.htm

12. ICQ: http://www.icq.com/

13. AOL Instant Messenger: http://www.aol.com/aim/

Simple Searches

With an estimated one billion pages and counting, it can be difficult to find exactly what you want on the web. You can reduce the time it takes by analyzing what you are looking for. If you are looking for web sites that focus on a particular subject, your best option is to use a web site that classifies many sites by subject. If you are looking for specific facts and figures, try an encyclopedia or a reference desk. If these don't work or your question is very specific, try a web search engine.

Web Site Classifications

Many searches involve fairly general questions such as "What web sites are there on sociology (or ethnomusicology)?" or "What web sites provide information on genealogy?" These kinds of questions are best answered by web sites that have classified a large number of web sites into subject categories and by topical guides to the web. The original subject classification of the web is Yahoo![1] It begins by dividing web sites into 14 categories ranging from "Arts & Humanities" to "News & Media" to "Society & Culture." Each of these categories is subdivided and subdivided again so that you can browse to increasingly specific kinds of sites. Yahoo! searches the subject categories as well as the web page titles and their descriptions. Yahoo! gathers information about new web sites from many sources and the creators of web sites usually notify Yahoo! of new web sites to add to the classification. There are other subject classification web sites, but in my experience Yahoo! is the most complete. Good guides for academic topics are the UniGuide Academic Guide to the Internet[2] and StudyWeb[3]. Using a subject classification web site is similar to the subject classification of your library catalog. You will find books relating to specific topics, but you will not necessarily find where a particular fact is located in the book.

The founders of the World Wide Web realized that information distributed all over the globe would be difficult to find unless there were some guides. They created the World Wide Web Virtual Library[4] by selecting volunteers to catalog major web sites for various subjects. If you look at the list of subjects, you will see that some categories are quite broad while others are quite specific. Since they are produced by volunteers whose workload varies, they may or may not be completely up-to-date. They are a good place to start, and often the sites are described more completely than the single line descriptions in Yahoo! Another useful resource for broad subject searches is the Argus Clearinghouse[5]. Throughout the web, people have spent time collecting information about web sites, mailing lists, and newsgroups. They compile this information into documents that are stored on the web and updated. The Argus Clearinghouse helps you to find these documents by cataloging them according to subject area, and by providing a summary and rating for each one.

25

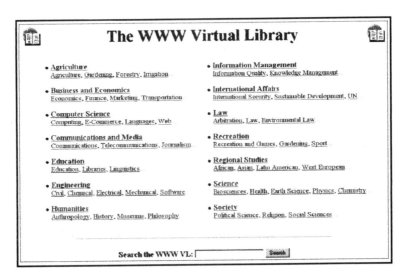

The WWW Virtual Library

- **Agriculture**
  Agriculture, Gardening, Forestry, Irrigation

- **Business and Economics**
  Economics, Finance, Marketing, Transportation

- **Computer Science**
  Computing, E-Commerce, Languages, Web

- **Communications and Media**
  Communications, Telecommunications, Journalism

- **Education**
  Education, Libraries, Linguistics

- **Engineering**
  Civil, Chemical, Electrical, Mechanical, Software

- **Humanities**
  Anthropology, History, Museums, Philosophy

- **Information Management**
  Information Quality, Knowledge Management

- **International Affairs**
  International Security, Sustainable Development, UN

- **Law**
  Arbitration, Law, Environmental Law

- **Recreation**
  Recreation and Games, Gardening, Sport

- **Regional Studies**
  African, Asian, Latin American, West European

- **Science**
  Biosciences, Health, Earth Science, Physics, Chemistry

- **Society**
  Political Science, Religion, Social Sciences

Search the WWW VL: [   ] [Search]

For sociology there are a number of subject guides. The best include the following: WCSU List: Sociology Internet Resources[6] a site maintained by Western Connecticut State University; the World Wide Web Virtual Library: Sociology[7]; which was established Dr. Samuel R. Brown and was updated by David Kincheloe. It is now maintained by Dr. Carl Cuneo, Dept. of Sociology, McMaster University, Hamilton, Ontario, Canada; and finally for a more global search, the SocioSite[8] based at the University of Amsterdam is an entire information system with subjects, sociologists, data archives, research tools and much more.

Facts and Figures

If you want to know the current ruler of a particular country or the population of the world explore one of the virtual reference desks or encyclopedias. A spectacular resource is Encyclopedia Britannica[9] which provides the full text of the encyclopedia and links to other resources on the web. My Virtual Reference Desk[10] and Martindale's 'The Reference Desk'[11] are the most extensive and complete of the reference desks. You will find links to a broad range of sources for factual information. Information Please[12] allows you to search its almanac, dictionary, and encyclopedia. Two good sources of information on other countries are the United Nations Infonation[13] by the UN (although the interface takes some practice) and E-Conflict's World Encyclopedia[14]. A good source of maps is National Geographic's Map Machine[15]. The Dead Sociologists Index[16] and Biography.com[17] provide capsule biographies for many of your favorite social thinkers and sociologists. The Ethnographic Atlas[18] at the University of Kent provides summary descriptions of about 60 societies.

Government publications, such as the CIA World Factbook[19] and the the Library of Congress Country Studies Series[20] are also available. From the U.S. Census you can download the tables from the Statistical Abstract of the U.S.[21] in Adobe Acrobat format.

Web Search Engines

As you become more specific about the information you want to find, you will probably turn to one of the search engines on the web that have indexed millions of web pages. Imagine if all the indexes from all the books in the library were combined into a single giant index. You could then find not only the book, but also the page you wanted in a single search. That is what search engines try to do. While Yahoo! classifies web sites, search engines index web pages. Most search engines also provide subject categories of web sites so that the difference between the two is blurring.

The indexes are constructed by software robots that travel around the web 24 hours a day discovering and indexing web pages. The coverage that each search engine offers is slightly different. Some try to be as comprehensive as possible, but no one engine has indexed all of the web pages. Altavista[22], and Fast Search[23] are recognized for the sizes of their databases. This means that they may index 350 million pages of the roughly one billion pages on the web. Brightgate[24] sends your query to several search engines and then combines the results. If you do not include several terms in your search, you will end up with thousands of pages containing the term you searched for. Each search engine has methods of restricting the search and each search engine has ways of ranking the results according to those that should be most useful to you. You should experiment with several. Some allow only relatively simple searches while others allow you to construct complex Boolean queries (you can find out what these are under Help on one of the big search engine home pages). NorthernLight[25] allows you to search a database of articles from journals in addition to searching web pages. You can then also purchase a copy of the article if it is not in your local library.

Web Links

1. Yahoo!: http://www.yahoo.com/
2. UniGuide Academic Guide to the Internet: http://www.aldea.com/guides/ag/attframes2.html
3. StudyWeb: http://www.studyweb.com/
4. World Wide Web Virtual Library: http://www.vlib.org/
5. Argus Clearinghouse: http://www.clearinghouse.net/
6. WCSU List: Sociology Internet Resources: http://www.ahs.cqu.edu.au/psysoc/soconline/html/onlinres.htm
7. World Wide Web Virtual Library: Sociology: http://www.mcmaster.ca/socscidocs/w3virtsoclib/index.htm
8. SocioSite: http://www.pscw.uva.nl/sociosite/index.html
9. Encyclopedia Britannica: http://www.britannica.com/
10. My Virtual Reference Desk: http://www.refdesk.com/
11. Martindale's 'The Reference Desk : http://www-sci.lib.uci.edu/HSG/Ref.html
12. Information Please Almanac: http://www.infoplease.com/index.html
13. Infonation: http://www.un.org/Pubs/CyberSchoolBus/infonation/e_infonation.htm
14. World Encyclopedia: http://www.emulateme.com/
15. Map Machine: http://www.nationalgeographic.com/resources/ngo/maps/
16. Dead Sociologists Index: http://raven.jmu.edu/~ridenelr/DSS/INDEX.HTML
17. Biography.com: http://www.biography.com/
18. Ethnographic Atlas: http://lucy.ukc.ac.uk/EthnoAtlas/ethno.html
19. CIA World Factbook: http://www.odci.gov/cia/publications/factbook/index.html
20. Country Studies Series: http://lcweb2.loc.gov/frd/cs/cshome.html
21. Statistical Abstract of the U.S.: http://www.census.gov/statab/www/
22. Altavista: http://altavista.digital.com/
23. Fast Search: http://www.alltheweb.com/
24. Brightgate: http://www.brightgate.com/
25. NorthernLight: http://www.northernlight.co

Research on the Web

The World Wide Web can help you improve your understanding of sociology by supplementing lectures, providing a context for the examples in the text, making you aware of current events that relate to the topics discussed in the text and in class, and giving you tools to increase the productivity of your research. The web is not a replacement for your campus library, but it can provide you with ready access to a great variety of information such as up-to-date statistics, maps, photos, or greater detail about topics covered briefly in the text. You can also query library catalogs (probably the catalog on your campus) to check the availability of books and articles.

Library Catalogs

Many colleges and universities have made their catalogs available for online access. While some may require a special program to access, increasingly they are designed for use with any web browser. The Academic Libraries[1] web index Yahoo! lists over 450 academic libraries around the world including Harvard University and Cambridge University. LibWeb[2] is even more comprehensive listing 3500 libraries in 100 countries. These catalogs can help you locate books in your campus library and can help you find references that are not available locally (so that you can request them through interlibrary loan). Library catalogs are a good place to find out what resources are available for a term paper topic or a presentation. Often they will also tell you if the book you need is checked out and when it is due back to the library.

Not really a library catalog, but nearly as useful are the web pages for booksellers such as Amazon.com[3]. If the book is no longer in print, try the used book search engines such as abebooks.com[4] and Bibliofind[5]. These sites allow you to search for books that are currently in print. They often provide a picture of the cover of the book and may include review comments and a table of contents. This can be particularly helpful if the book you need is not at your library and you don't have enough time to get it through interlibrary loan.

Online Books

A number of books and articles are available directly on the Internet. You can download them to a disk and read them at your leisure. While reading a book on a computer screen is not as pleasant as reading a physical book, it does have one advantage. With an online book, you can search for any word or phrase. This is useful if you think that the author mentions a topic that you are interested in, but you don't want to read the whole book to find a single phrase or paragraph. Because of copyright restrictions, most online books are older books whose copyright has expired. It is a good place to look for works that are primarily of historical interest such as the works of Charles Darwin, Herbert Spencer, or Karl Marx. The Internet Public Library[6] and The Online Books Page[7] let you search thousands of online titles including books and shorter pieces. For books relating to the United States, try Making of America[8], a collection of 1,600 books and 50,000 articles relating to American social history published during the nineteenth century.

Journals and Journal Indexes

To locate recently published articles relating to a particular topic, check UnCover[9], a database of current article information taken from well over 17,000 multi-disciplinary journals spanning the years from 1988 to the present. A relatively new web search site NorthernLight[10] allows you to search for magazine articles and order copies over the web. Sociological Research Online[11] publishes high quality applied sociology, focusing on theoretical, empirical and methodological discussions which engage with current political, cultural and intellectual topics and debates. The University of Chicago Press [12] has made the table of contents for the American Journal of Sociology available on line as well as an electronic edition of Public Opinion Quarterly. Other indices such as the Social Sciences Periodical Index or Current Contents on the web are available as subscription services. However, many academic libraries subscribe to these services so you may be able to search them by connecting to your university library web page.

More and more university libraries are subscribing to electronic versions of professional journals. Electronic versions of a journal allow you to download an article in Adobe Acrobat® format. You can print out the article or read it on your computer screen. You should find out what journals your library gets in electronic format since it can save you a trip to the library and the information is available 24 hours a day, 7 days a week.

Writing Resources

When you have to write a paper, there are several web resources that can help answer your questions about grammar and style, copyright and fair use, and how to cite digital information. A great place to start is Dushkin/ McGraw-Hill's How to Write Term Papers[13] written by John T. Rourke. An old standby writing style manual by William Strunk is available on the Net, the 1918 version of *The Elements of Style.*[14] For questions about grammar you can try two different handbooks on the web. The Grammar Handbook[15] at the University of Illinois Urbana Champaign and the On-Line English Grammar[16] by the Digital Education Network.

If an idea is not yours you need to cite its source. Dartmouth College has a nice web site called Sources: Their Use and Acknowledgment[17] that will give you the basics. How do you cite electronic resources? The Modern Language Association (MLA) has the basics at MLA Style[18] for one widely used approach. The American Psychological Association in Electronic Reference Formats[19] describes another approach.

If you need more details about copyright and fair use, try Fair Use of Copyrighted Works[20] by the Consortium for Educational Technology for University Systems (CETUS). The U.S. Copyright Office, FAQ[21] has a page with answers to your frequently asked questions as well.

Web Links

1. Academic Libraries:
   http://www.yahoo.com/Reference/Libraries/Academic_Libraries/
2. LibWeb: http://sunsite.berkeley.edu/Libweb/
3. Amazon.com: http://www.amazon.com/
4. abebooks.com: http://www.abebooks.com/
5. Bibliofind: http://www.bibliofind.com/
6. Internet Public Library: http://www.ipl.org/
7. The Online Books Page: http://www.cs.cmu.edu/books.html
8. Making of America: http://www.umdl.umich.edu/moa/
9. UnCover: http://uncweb.carl.org/
10. NorthernLight: http://www.northernlight.com/
11. Sociological Research Online: http://www.socresonline.org.uk/
12. The University of Chicago Press: http://www.journals.uchicago.edu/
13. How to Write Term Papers:
    http://www.dushkin.com/online/study/dgen2.mhtml
14. *The Elements of Style*: http://www.bartleby.com/141/index.html
15. Grammar Handbook:
    http://www.english.uiuc.edu/cws/wworkshop/grammarmenu.htm
16. On-Line English Grammar: http://www.edunet.com/english/grammar/index.html
17. Sources: Their Use and Acknowledgment:
    http://www.dartmouth.edu/~sources/index.html
18. MLA Style: http://www.mla.org/style/sources.htm
19. Electronic Reference Formats: http://www.apa.org/journals/webref.html
20. Fair Use of Copyrighted Works: http://www.cetus.org/fairindex.html
21. U.S. Copyright Office, FAQ: http://lcweb.loc.gov/copyright/faq.html

Current Events

You can follow current events on the web by visiting the web pages of newspapers and broadcast news organizations. For national and world news my favorites are ABC News[1], BBC News[2], and The New York Times[3], but try others to see which ones you prefer. The New York Times requires that you register to browse the site, but registration is free. You can find an extensive listing of online U. S. papers at US Newspaper Links[4]. There are many other news sites on the web from all over the world. You should be able to locate them at Yahoo!

To find other news stories, you can visit a topical news page or use a news search engine. Topical news pages provide links to news items covering a particular subject. For links to news stories that relate to all aspects of sociology visit SocioNews[5]. This page based out of Great Britain contains current headlines as well as links to scores of news sources, journals and internet links from Europe and the U.S. Other topical news pages include Artigen[6] and NewsHub[7].

News search engines allow you to search recent news stories that include a particular word or phrase in the title or in the text of the story. Most news web sites allow you to search their site, but some charge for retrieving older stories from their archives. There are a couple of search engines that search over several sites. These include NewsTracker[8] by Excite and TotalNews[9]

www.newshub.com

Web Links

1. ABC News: http://www.abcnews.com/
2. BBC News: http://news.bbc.co.uk/default.htm
3. The New York Times: http://www.nytimes.com/
4. US Newspaper Links: http://www.usnewspaperlinks.com/
5. SocioNews: http://www.sociologyonline.f9.co.uk/Socionews.htm
6. Artigen: http://www.artigen.com/
7. NewsHub: http://www.newshub.com/
8. NewsTracker : http://nt.excite.com/
9. TotalNews: http://www.totalnews.com/

Learning

There are a number of ways to learn on the net. One simple way is to subscribe to mailing lists or to monitor newsgroups on subjects that you want to learn more about. There are also a variety of short tutorials on the web that help you to learn about the Internet, the world wide web, and how to create web pages. Microsoft has tutorial pages for the Internet and the web (Internet Guide & Web Tutorial[1]). A nice set of tutorials on how to develop your own web resources is Webmonkey: A How To Guide for Web Developers[2].

From online courses to textbook specific sites, there are hundreds of sociology learning experiences on the web. As you will discover, the great majority of these resources have been created as supplements to college courses. Sociology Online[3] provides quizzes, slideshows and a gallery of social thinkers. Free-Ed.net[4] is in the process of creating a number of free sociology tutorials and resources. Currently they offer an online tutorial in social psychology. for different topics in biosociology and cultural sociology. Washington State University is producing a number of online learning modules. Try their What is Culture?[5] module for a subject outline, discussions, student hypertext presentations and a glossary. At the World Lecture Hall[6] you can find online course materials for sociology courses arranged according to major topics (and for other subjects as well).

Online courses include longer, more formal sequences of material. Your university may offer distance education courses that you can take just as you would any other course. Online courses usually charge tuition. There are several consortia that provide information on distance education offerings for a number of universities. The largest include the Western Governors University[7], the Southern Regional Electronic Campus[8], the Committee on Institutional Cooperation: Common Market of Courses and Institutions[9] [midwestern universities], and the Community College Distance Learning Network[10]. Before you sign up for a course check to see that the course is accredited by a recognized accreditation organization and that your university will accept transfer credit for the course.

Web Links

1. Internet Guide & Web Tutorial:
   http://www.microsoft.com/insider/internet/default.htm

2. Webmonkey: A How To Guide for Web Developers:
   http://www.hotwired.com/webmonkey/

3. Sociology Online: http://www.sociologyonline.f9.co.uk/Home4NN.htm

4. Free-Ed.net: http://www.free-ed.net/fr09/fr0907.htm

5. What is Culture?:
   http://www.wsu.edu:8001/vcwsu/commons/topics/culture/culture-index.html

6. World Lecture Hall: http://www.utexas.edu/world/lecture/

7. Western Governors University: http://www.wgu.edu/

8. Southern Regional Electronic Campus: http://www.srec.sreb.org/

9. Committee on Institutional Cooperation: Common Market of Courses and Institutions: http://www.cic.uiuc.edu/CMCI/cmci_homepage.htm

10. Community College Distance Learning Network: http://ccdln.rio.maricopa.edu/

PART II.
RESEARCHING SOCIOLOGY ON THE WEB

Introduction

The Internet has opened up new frontiers for teaching, learning and conducting research. Information about the social world has never been more accessible. Learning about sociology has become more hands-on with the availability of web-based instruction, data collections, and mailing lists. Teaching about the social world can engage students in more active experiences by using the Internet. Of course it goes without saying that research possibilities have expanded tremendously with the advent of virtual libraries and search engines.

My own experiences teaching sociology have convinced me of the efficacy of incorporating Internet activities into course work. Feedback from students who use the Internet in their assignments is consistently positive. Using Internet assignments I have found that students retain more information, are more willing to enter into class discussions and are generally more engaged in the learning process.

The Internet and the information it can access is a monumental phenomenon in itself. In fact, it is one that continues to grow exponentially every day. Students of sociology can easily become overwhelmed with the task of surfing the Internet. Instructors may find it difficult to incorporate new Internet learning activities into their courses. This guide has been designed to help both teachers and students use the Internet more effectively in the learning process. In this section you will find current and relevant web sites organized into the major fields within the discipline of sociology. These are starting points for more successful and enriching experiences on the web.

I have come to believe that when we are actively engaged in the learning process we are much more successful at achieving our goals. The Internet can easily be used to incorporate more active learning into the curriculum. For most students it's becoming a tool they are using in other aspects of their lives. We are all moving from a written culture to an image culture. The internet is a big part of the cultural shift. Using it as a learning tool is a way to stay with the curve.

The Study of Society

While putting this guide together I discovered several comprehensive web sites that could be used as gateways into the field – as it exists on the Internet. If you're just getting into the virtual world of research on the Internet or you're a student who's searching for topics for a research paper, these are essential starting points. Michael C. Kearl who is at Trinity University in San

37

Antonio has constructed an excellent site that I refer to throughout this guide. He calls it a Tour Through Cyber Society[1] and it's just that. Many of his pages can be incorporated into sociology courses. His information is presented in a highly readable format with Internet links to all kinds of other related sites interspersed throughout each page. The Social Science Hub and the Sociology Web Hawg are two other wonderful starting points for research. Each is comprehensive enough to include many of the major categories within the discipline. All these Internet addresses should be book-marked on your computer.

SOCIOLOGY WEB HAWG

Web Links

1. Tour Through Cyber Society: http://www.trinity.edu/mkearl/index.html
2. Social Science Hub: http://www2.dynamite.com.au/kiwisunf/ss.htm
3. Sociology Web Hog: http://rock.uwc.edu/~pgroth/sochawg.htm

One of the most popular sites among students and instructors alike has been The Dead Sociologist's Society[1] constructed by Larry Ridener currently at James Mason University. On the web page you will be able to access the Dead Sociologists Index where you will find biographical sketches, a summary of ideas and examples of original work for most of the significant classical social thinkers. This is one of the most comprehensive theory sites out there. In addition to an index of classical social thinkers, you will find images, lectures, passages from core texts, and a very comprehensive list of sociology links. This site makes a great companion to introductory texts in social theory.

Surfing these pages are a good way for students to prepare for exams, complete background searches for writing research papers, and collecting data for class presentations. I have been able to use this site to collect extensive information for class discussions. Students also have found this site to be very useful for writing papers about the development of significant ideas. My students report that they feel like they have a better grasp of the material after spending time actively engaged in learning projects that send them to the Internet. You will also find at this site a link to a paper presented by Ridener entitled; *The Good, The Bad, And The Ugly in Cyberspace: Ups and Downs of the Dead Sociologist's Society*. It's a very good account of his own experiences using the web to teach sociology.

Sociology Online[2] provides another wonderful web page full of information about both classical and contemporary social thinkers. This British site contains indexes, biographies, photographs, references, texts, chat rooms, quizzes, slideshows and a set of links to relevant sites. The site offers online instruction in a number of sociological fields. The theory section allows students to study lecture notes and then choose from a number of quizzes or play sociology hangman. While the site does include foundational information about classical theory it's the contemporary and postmodern theory emphasis that will help students most. It would be easy to spend hours in these pages. I would recommend it as course supplement to contemporary theory classes to be used for reference and tutorials throughout the semester.

The University of Amsterdam has a comprehensive site called SocioSite[3] that includes references to 73 classical and contemporary sociologists as well as links to specific theories and homepages of practicing sociologists. On these pages you will find an index of 167 subject categories in sociology. These pages are going to provide you with a real global perspective in sociology by allowing access to a number of European theorists that might not be available to students any other way.

The above sites are appropriate for undergraduate students who are just beginning to explore social theory as well as graduate students who are ready to delve deeper in their reading and exploring. The sites are wide-ranging enough so that students can make comparisons among thinkers and many of the core ideas in social theory. These sites are constructed in such a way as to afford the researcher with some fun and adventure - even with social theory!

For more advanced study and for graduate students there are any number of web pages that specifically target social theory in much more detail. Many include actual selections from important works in social theory. There are also links to the web pages of contemporary sociologists across the globe. It's possible for your students to engage in dialogue with sociologists at other universities and with other students in related chat rooms.

The Sociology Café[4] has a page for sociological theories that link to the web pages of sociologists at universities around the world. Included in this web site are critical thinking questions and an on-line community for discussions related to social theory. For online texts of classical social thinkers go to the University of Chicago's Classical Sociology Theory[5] site. So often students are trapped in reading secondary sources. If your class text does not contain the primary sources you're looking for, this is an excellent source to search through. The Voice of the Shuttle[6] site has references to a wide range of current sociological thinkers many specifically oriented toward cultural theories. The site contains links to Millennium Studies, Generation Wars, Culture Wars, Popular and Mass Culture to name a few. For more detailed research about specific theories and social thinkers try these sites: The Marxists Internet Archive[7], The Marxism Page[8], George's Page[9] (George Herbert Mead), Cooley's The Looking Glass Self,[10] The Durkheim Pages[11], Michel Foucault[12], Power And Bureaucracy[13] (Weber). Verstehen: Max Weber's Homepage[14].

Another fabulous Weber site is the Protestant Ethic and the Spirit of Capitalism[15] created by Japanese sociologist Moriyuki Abukuma. The web page focuses on this pivotal economic theory Weber used to wrestle with the ghost of Marx. The page contains an outline, the original text and commentary by Abukuma – all in three separate windows appearing on the screen simultaneously. Please see similar references to Weber in the section on Social Organizations and Institutions.

The Durkheim Pages

www.lang.uiuc.edu/durkheim/index.html

Jessica Champlin has created and maintains a site called Sociology Resources on the Net (SocioRealm[16]) where you can find links to sites on Marx, Durkheim, Simmel, Weber and Rousseau, as well as more extensive links to contemporary theorists such as Baudrillard, Becker, Berger, Goffman, Merton, and Parsons. The site also includes links to several postmodernist pages. This would be good place to start an exploration of modern social theory and move backwards to see the links with classical foundations. An entire class project could be accomplished from this one web site.

The internet has several sites specific to the major sociological paradigms. These are great places to send students for an exploration mission. They will discover the major figures in the field and be exposed to important terms and concepts. Many of these sites represent academic societies that are open for membership. Students should be encouraged to pursue their intellectual interests by interacting with others through the internet. The Society for the Study of Symbolic Interactionism[17] has papers, on-line discussions, and teaching resources. The University of Regina has an online course page with notes on Structural-Functionalism and Parsons[18] Anyone who has tried to read Parsons would appreciate any notes on the subject. The University of Alabama has pages up on the world wide web that are designed by students for students. From their anthropology department you will find a very comprehensive page on Functionalism[19] containing vocabulary, references, key figures, and basic premises.

Take a look at the World Socialist Web[20] to find out how people are putting Marxist and socialist theory to use in real world political situations. The site contains editorials, news reports, and scholarly papers. What better way to see how people have put theory into practice? Cultural Logic[21] is an electronic journal of Marxist theory and practice. At this site you will find interviews, book reviews, and articles all in the vein of Marxist theory. Students can scan this web site to learn about current issues that Marxist theory seeks to address.

Finally, if you will go the <u>Spoons Webpage</u>[22] you will find ongoing discussions about political and philosophical issues. This is a list site that you sign up for and that allows you to take part in ongoing discussions. There are a number of lists that pertain to contemporary social theory such as Baudrillard, culture, the Frankfurt School, or women in the third world. The site currently has several open lists. You could begin your own social theory discussion topic.

Web Links

1. The Dead Sociologist's Society:
   http://raven.jmu.edu/~ridenelr/DSS/DEADSOC.HTML
2. Sociology Online: http://www.sociologyonline.co.uk/Home4NN.htm
3. SocioSite: http://www.pscw.uva.nl/sociosite/topics/sociologists.html
4. Sociology Café:
   http://www.geocities.com/Athens/Olympus/2147/basetheory.html
5. Classical Sociological Theory:
   http://www.spc.uchicago.edu/ssr1/PRELIMS/theory.html
6. The Voice of the Shuttle:
   http://vos.ucsb.edu/shuttle/cultural.html#authors
7. The Marxists Internet Archive:
   http://csf.colorado.edu/mirrors/marxists.org/
8. The Marxism Page: http://www.anu.edu.au/polsci/marx/marx.html
9. George's Page: http://paradigm.soci.brocku.ca/~lward/default.html
10. The Looking Glass Self:
    http://raven.jmu.edu/~ridenelr/courses/LKGLSSLF.HTML
11. The Durkheim Pages: http://www.lang.uiuc.edu/durkheim/
12. Michel Foucault: http://www.synaptic.bc.ca/ejournal/foucault.htm
13. Power and Bureaucracy:
    http://sol.brunel.ac.uk/~jarvis/bola/power/bureau.html
14. The Protestant Ethic and the Spirit of Capitalism: http://www.asahi-net.or.jp/~hw8m-mrkm/weber/world/ethic/pro_eth_frame.html
15. Verstehen:Max Weber's Webpage:
    http://msumusik.mursuky.edu/~felwell/http/weber/whome.htm
16. SocioRealm: http://www.geocities.com/CollegePark/Quad/5889/
17. Society for the Study of Symbolic Interactionism:
    http://sun.soci.niu.edu/~sssi/
18. Structural Functionalism and Parsons:
    http://uregina.ca/~gingrich/n2f99.htm
19. Functionalism: http://www.as.ua.edu/ant/Faculty/murphy/function.htm
20. World Socialist Web: http://www.wsws.org/
21. Cultural Logic: http://eserver.org/clogic/
22. Spoon Homepage: http://lists.village.virginia.edu/~spoons/

Research Methods

In this section I want to introduce you to several sites that can be useful as you begin to do research. The other sections of this guide will provide you with web pages related to specific research findings. This section contains Internet sites to assist you with your research methods.

Students at Cornell University have put together a web page containing Research Methods Tutorials[1]. The lessons include sampling, field research multivariate analysis and analysis of variance techniques. Linda Lambert has put together a web page called Methods and Measurements[2] that serves as a great primer for foundational statistical procedures. In addition to clearly presented definitions and tutorials the site has clever graphics and an extensive list of methodological links and online statistical tools. This site is a gem and should be book-marked on your computer.

There are a number of Internet sites that will help you with statistical calculations. One of the best sites is called StatPages.net[3] where you will find a guide to pages that help you perform statistical calculations from ANOVA, cross-tabs and regression analyses. When you are introducing statistics to your classes, whether in an introductory class or a full-blown research methods class, you could use these students as a introduction to some of the most essential statistical procedures used in the social sciences. What I find most useful is finding ways to get students to be actively involved in the learning process. For so many students statistics may seem like a foreign language. Resources such as these pages help students to get their hands dirty and allow them a great opportunity for practice. Other useful statistical sites include: Basic Statistics[4] (designed for reporters), Bill Trochim's Center for Social Research Methods [5] (lots of stuff!), and the UCLA Statistics Textbook [6].

The University of Surrey (U.K.) electronically publishes the Social Research Update[7]. Each issue covers one topic in sufficient depth to indicate the main directions of recent developments in social research and provide a bibliography for further reading. The web page currently contains an archive of the past 30 issues. Issues on the site range from analyzing qualitative data by computer to telephone interviewing.

Using the Internet as a source of information for research papers has led to all kinds of problems with citation formats. A Student's Guide to Referencing On-line Information Sources in the Social Sciences[8] is another handy site that should be book-marked on your computer. This site provides examples of proper citation of on-line information using the APA, MLA, and Chicago styles. William Patterson University has a brief version of the APA style format on its Guide for Citing Electronic Information[9] web page

The Social Science Paper Publisher[10] is an international, informal electronic journal that seeks to electronically publish broadly sociological writings and research. While you're working on that research paper you should check into the American Sociological Association's Style Guidelines and Manuscript Preparation Checklist[11]. This is a pdf file and you will need to have the right plug in device to download it. Your search engine should automatically suggest options for you.

Several of the more comprehensive sociology sites on the Internet have links to methodological web pages. The SocioSite[12] at the University of Amsterdam has links to global research centers, data archives and search tools. Two other large sites with extensive research methodology links are: A Sociological Tour Through Cyberspace[13], and The Dead Sociologist's Society[14]. These are good places to start especially if you are taking a research methods course and want to see some actual research. The Survey Research Center at Princeton[15] is a university based comprehensive site with links to web based research programs, data sets, methodologies, and leading research centers and organizations in the U.S.

There are a number of research organizations that have web sites. Accessing any of these pages will give you a good idea of the breadth and scope of research currently being conducted by some of the largest organizations in the country. The National Opinion Research Center[16] (NORC) conducts survey research in the public interest for government agencies, educational institutions, private foundations, non-profit organizations, and private corporations. At the NORC site you will find information about the General Social Survey (GSS). The mission of the GSS is to make timely, high-quality, scientifically relevant data available to the social science research community. Since 1972 the GSS has conducted 22 independent cross-sectional surveys of the adult household population of the United States. These surveys have been widely distributed and extensively analyzed by social scientists around the world. To date, NORC has documented the publication of more than 4,500 articles using the data.

The Gallup Research Center[17] at the University of Nebraska at Lincoln - concentrates on all areas of survey research and quantitative methods, including public opinion, consumer and employee satisfaction, and data utilization in the workplace. Visit this web site to learn about recent symposiums conducted on research methodology. The Indiana University at Bloomington[18] has a social science research facility that focuses on academic, social science, and public policy research. From this page you can link to dozens of research entities sponsored by the university. The Institute for Public Opinion Research[19] (IPOR) at Florida International University provides professional services in all aspects of survey research including study and sample design, questionnaire development, interviewing, data entry, data analysis, and report writing. From their web page you can view public opinion polls conducted in Florida and among Cuban Americans. There are also some helpful research oriented links. Finally, the Survey

Research Center[20] of the Institute for Social Research (University of Michigan) conducts interdisciplinary social science research involving the collection or analysis of data from scientific sample surveys. The page contains an index of research projects. Each research project has its own web page that you can access directly from the index.

There are any number of data sets out there on the Internet that are excellent sources for teaching research methods and statistics. These can also be excellent sources for students to use to conduct secondary data analyses. These sites include: The National Science Foundation[21] (Social, Behavioral and Economic Research), The Inter-University Consortium for Political and Social Research[22], The National Archives and Records Administration Center for Electronic Records[23], The Census Bureau[24], Federal Statistics[25] (70 Agencies), and of course, The World Database of Happiness[26].

The Survey Research Institute at Princeton

Web Links

1. Research Methods Tutorials:
   http://trochim.human.cornell.edu/tutorial/TUTORIAL.HTM

2. Methods and Measurements:
   http://csbs.utsa.edu/social&policy/soc/masters/meth_meas.html

3. StatPages.net: http://members.aol.com/johnp71/javastat.html

4. Basic Statistics: www.robertniles.com

5. Bill Trochim's Center for Social Research Methods:
   http://trochim.human.cornell.edu/index.html

6. UCLA Statistics Textbook: http://home.stat.ucla.edu/textbook/

7. Social Research Update: http://www.soc.surrey.ac.uk/sru/Sru.html

8. A Student's Guide to Referencing On-line Information Sources in the
   Social Sciences: http://cua6.csuohio.edu/~ernie/courses/cite.htm

9. Guide for Citing Electronic Information:
   http://www.wpunj.edu/wpcpages/library/citing.htm

10. The Social Science Paper Publisher: http://www.sspp.net/

11. American Sociological Association's Style Guidelines and Manuscript
    Preparation Checklist: asanet.org/pubs/notice.pdf

12. SocioSite: http://www.pscw.uva.nl/sociosite/index.html

13. A Sociological Tour Through Cyberspace:
    http://www.trinity.edu/mkearl/index.html

14. The Dead Sociologist's Society:
    http://raven.jmu.edu/~ridenelr/DSS/DEADSOC.HTML

15. National Opinion Research Center: http://www.norc.uchicago.edu/

16. Gallup Research Center: http://www.unl.edu/unl-grc/

17. Indiana University at Bloomington:
    http://www.iub.edu/academic/centers.html

18. Institute for Public Opinion Research: http://www.fiu.edu/orgs/ipor/

19. The Survey Research Center at Princeton:
    http://www.princeton.edu/~abelson/

20. Survey Research Center: http://www.isr.umich.edu/src/

21. The National Science Foundation (Social, Behavioral and Economic
    Research): www.nsf.gov/sbe/redirect.htm

22. The Inter-University Consortium for Political and Social Research:
    www.icpsr.umich.edu/

23. National Archives and Records Administration Center for Electronic
    Records: www.nara.gov/nara/electronic/

24. Census Bureau: www.census.gov/

25. Federal Statistics: www.fedstats.gov/
26. World Database of Happiness: www.eur.nl/fsw/research/happiness/

Culture

To begin to understand the social world you need to be able to see the basic patterns that exist. Social theory helps us to understand the ideas behind the study of the social world. Methodology examines the ways in which we go about our study. The most basic of patterns that students of society encounter is culture. The study of culture is usually one of the first lessons that sociologists teach. To view papers, presentations and lectures on culture go to <u>Sociology Online</u>[1] and <u>World Lecture Hall: Sociology</u>[2]. Here you will find links to information that can supplement course readings on culture and provide current research on topics related to culture.

What follows are internet sites that will introduce to you the basic elements of culture, let you explore world cultures, help you to examine multiculturalism and finally take you through a tour of popular and postmodern culture research and thought.

In the way of basic introductions, look at the culture web page for the encyclopedia Britannica at <u>Britannica.com</u>[3]. Here students will get a feel for the meaning of culture. At the University of Minnesota's Center for Advanced Research on Language Acquisition <u>What is Culture?</u>[4] Web page, you will be introduced to a number of definitions across many academic disciplines. Washington State University sponsors another <u>What is Culture (WSU)</u>[5] web page with basic definitions of culture and an index of writings on culture by great thinkers such as Clifford Geertz and cultural discussions on topics like "women, culture and power".

General resources for studying culture can be found at the <u>CIA World Fact Book</u>[6] and at the <u>Library of Congress Country Studies</u>[7]. Both sites can be used to collect basic information about cultures from all over the world. Using sites like these make comparison and contrast studies more productive. Students taking a culture studies course should bookmark these sites on their computers. Add them to your course syllabus as useful resources

We need to rely on our friends in anthropology if we're going to get a comprehensive understanding of the history and meaning of culture. A Sociology Guy's Anthropology Links[8] ought to do the trick, as would the Kinship and Social Organization[9] web page. Both of these would be tremendous sites for out of class projects or writing papers. The Ancient World Web[10] and Washington State University's World Civilizations[11] web site will provide you with information and numerous links related to history and global civilization. These are great sites for students who have had no experience with anthropology or with much history (believe it or not it's possible to graduate from college these days without taking a history course!). Finally, About.com[12] has a culture index page that has links to most of the world cultures. This information would be useful in making the transition from basic culture concepts like cultural universals and folkways to current issues and debates related to multiculturalism.

Multiculturalism is a hot topic these days. You'll probably cover it in your sociology classes. Some supplemental Internet sites include the Multicultural Homepage[13], a new site that is putting together cultural backgrounds for the diverse populations living here in the U.S. and other regions of the world. The Multicultural Pavilion[14] is a resource page for educators, students and activists. Links provide information about a variety of cultural experiences, discussion forums, learning activities, and mailing lists for interested "activists." This site would be especially useful for projects targeted specifically at multicultural issues in education.

What makes cultural studies fun is taking a look at popular culture. Students always get more involved when we cover these kinds of topics that are easily recognizable in their every day lives. Some excellent comprehensive sites that one could spend hours in are Sarah Zupko's popcultures.com[15] and Cultural Studies Central[16]. Both sites provide opportunities for joining discussion groups. The sites include debates, resources, links, magazines, book reviews, and academic connections. Students would learn a great deal about pop culture and postmodernity by just surfing through either of these sites. They are great places for exploration and discovery.

The Center for the Study of Popular Culture[17] web page will connect you with resources related to politics, media, and the entertainment culture. Current thoughts and opinions about the state of Western culture are explored on a number of levels in many of the related sites. On a lighter note, the History of Cinema and Pop Culture[18] web page is a creative British product that explores the relationship between film and popular culture. The site has record of the collection of the Bill Douglas Centre of the History of Cinema and Pop Culture at the University of Exeter. There are a number of links to related sites and to web pages of staff and students of the Centre and the Department of English. Of course, when it comes to pop culture the Internet itself is probably one of the best learning tools. There are whole programs now developing on the Sociology of the Internet. As long as you're researching pop culture you might as well check out the Elvis Spotter's Website[19]. A successful teaching tool is to have students construct their own web pages. The Elvis Spotter's Website could be used as a model for students to use in constructing their own web page that addresses significant elements of pop culture.

Web Links

1. Sociological Research Online: http://www.socresonline.org.uk/
2. World Lecture Hall: Sociology: http://www.utexas.edu/world/lecture/soc/
3. Britannica.com: http://search.britannica.com/search?query=culture
4. What is Culture?: http://carla.acad.umn.edu/culture.html
5. What is Culture: http://www.wsu.edu:8001/vcwsu/commons/topics/culture/culture-index.html
6. CIA World Fact Book: http://www.odci.gov/cia/publications/factbook/index.html
7. The Library of Congress Country Studies: http://lcweb2.loc.gov/frd/cs/cshome.html
8. A Sociology Guy's Anthropology Links: http://www.trinity.edu/~mkearl/anthro.html
9. Kinship and Social Organization: http://www.umanitoba.ca/anthropology/tutor/
10. The Ancient World Web: http://www.julen.net/ancient/
11. Washington State University World Civilizations: http://www.wsu.edu:8000/~dee/
12. About.com Culture Index: http://home.about.com/culture/index.htm?PM=59_0216_T
13. Multicultural Homepage: http://pasture.ecn.purdue.edu/~agenhtml/agenmc/
14. Multicultural Pavilion: http://curry.edschool.virginia.edu/go/multicultural/
15. popcultures.com: http://www.popcultures.com/
16. Cultural Studies Central: http://www.culturalstudies.net/
17. Center for the Study of Popular Culture: www.cspc.org
18. History of Cinema and Pop Culture: http://www.ex.ac.uk/bill.douglas/menu.html
19. Elvis Spotter's Website: http://fs.dai.net/ac/616480/N03.html?http://www.seanmccormick.com/Elvis

Social Groups and Institutions

Organizations

One of the best ways to study society is to look at the groups it creates. These kinds of groups can be categorized in a number of ways. There are both formal and informal types of groupings that we are all a part of. The Formal Organizations[1] web site at the University of Chicago provides summaries of major work in the field of organizational behavior and organizations. This is a great way to expose students to the work of leading thinkers without having to buy numerous textbooks. It's a low cost way to expand the reading options for your course. Another site, the Historical Background of Organizational Behavior[2] prepared by Edward G. Wertheim of the College of Business Administration, Northeastern University, provides a good introductory background and addresses many of the major works in the field. This is a good site to surf if you're just starting to study human organizations and want to learn what the business people are studying. If you've taken a course or two in French there's a web page called History of the Discipline[3]. It contains a series of interviews with influential scientists in the field of organizational behavior. The interviews themselves are in English but there's a lot more here if you can read French!

Complexity, Complex Systems & Chaos Theory, Organizations as Self-Adaptive Complex Systems[4] is a real mouthful! But the site contains useful information for people wanting to investigate organizations as complex systems. Included on the site is a comprehensive listing of related web sites, journals in the field, working papers, tools for doing organizational analyses and lecture notes. You'll find several web sources out there that address learning organizations – one of the latest trends in organizational theory. The Learning Organization[5] is a collection of web papers in the field of learning organizations and leadership. Another similar site that includes.a number of useful resources and links is the Learning Organization Resources on the Web and on the Net[6] web site. It includes web links, web papers, book reviews and conference announcements. If you're ready to begin a serious study of how our culture is being socialized into an organizational culture then you might want to join the Society for Organizational Learning[7] – or at least visit. This is a comprehensive site that provides information about resources, consultants, online courses, and organizational links. Any of these web pages would make a fascinating cultural study in themselves.

Web Links

1. Formal Organizations:
   http://www.src.uchicago.edu/ssr1/PRELIMS/orgs.htm

2. Historical Background of Organizational Behavior:
   http://www.cba.neu.edu/~ewertheim/introd/history.htm#Theoryx

3. History of the Discipline: http://www.cso.edu/memoire_a.htm

4. Complexity, Complex Systems & Chaos Theory, Organizations as Self-Adaptive Complex Systems: http://www.brint.com/Systems.htm

5. Learning Organization:
   www.newgrange.com/dfoffice/learning_organization.htm

6. Learning Organization Resources on the Web and on the Net:
   http://www.gpsi.com/lo.html

7. Society for Organizational Learning: http://www.sol-ne.org/

The Department of Labor[1] web site contains links to a multitude of government resources. Especially helpful might be the library section that will provide you with Bureau of Labor Statistics[2] reports, speeches, policy papers, and congressional testimony. These comprehensive government sites are great places to take Internet tours in order to familiarize you with "what's out there."

While you're at the Department of Labor take a look at the Department of Labor National Longitudinal Surveys[3], which provide links to a number of research data sets related to the world of work. Included on the site are a series of research papers based on the DOL research findings. These are excellent resources for not only studies of the economic behavior but for research methods courses as well. Similarly, the Federal Statistics[4] web site offers comprehensive statistical reports on a wide range of social categories. At this site you can find statistical reports from just about every federal agency that collects social statistics. From this site you will also find links to other statistical reports such as the Statistical Abstract of the United States and the State and Metropolitan Area Data Book. Students new to the social sciences might find the Kids Pages useful as a primer for getting their feet wet.

When you're ready to really get into some serious economic data, go to the National Bureau of Economic Research[5] web page. This organization is a private, nonprofit, nonpartisan research organization dedicated to promoting a greater understanding of how the economy works. This page reflects research conducted by more than 500 university professors around the country who are the leading scholars in their fields.

Most sociological studies of the economy begin with looking at the income of individuals and families. The Panel Study of Income Dynamics[6] is a longitudinal survey of a representative sample of U.S. individuals and the families in which they reside. It has been ongoing since 1968. The data are collected annually, and the data files contain the full span of information collected over the course of the study. PSID data can be used for cross-sectional, longitudinal, and intergenerational analysis and for studying both individuals and families. The Federal Reserve Bank in Minneapolis put together a site that links visitors to the National Reserve System, research papers, and analyses of the U.S. economy including forecasts - Economic Research and Data[7]. If you've not taken an economics course this site may well provide you with some basic information that could be incorporated into presentations – including charts and graphs.

When you get tired of scanning numbers, charts and graphs you might want to take a look at the History of Economic Thought Website[8] which has an extensive *Schools of Thought* section that provides a more than thorough curriculum in economic philosophy. This is a wonderful site that acts as a contrast to all the statistical reports that have come before.

Web Links

1. Department of Labor: http://www.dol.gov/
2. Bureau of Labor Statistics: http://stats.bls.gov/
3. Department of Labor National Longitudinal Surveys: http://stats.bls.gov/nlshome.htm
4. Federal Statistics: http://www.fedstats.gov/
5. National Bureau of Economic Research: http://www.nber.org/data_index.html
6. Panel Study of Income Dynamics: http://www.isr.umich.edu/src/psid/index.html
7. Economic Research and Data: http://woodrow.mpls.frb.fed.us/economy/
8. History of Economic Thought Website: http://cepa.newschool.edu/het/

Education

The U.S. Dept. of Education[1] website is the first place one should access when doing research about education. The site contains current and past educational statistics as well as assessment reports and program evaluations. At comprehensive sites such as this students can not only see current research findings but also use the reports on the site as models for constructing their own research papers and projects. Education World[2] is a site that looks like it's designed for professional educators. What better place for social scientists to begin constructing an ethnography of our learning culture. While this doesn't appear to be an entirely objective site, it is one of the largest collections of issues, educational findings, reports, interviews and current events related to American schools.

To immediately access current and past data on education in America go to the National Center for Education Statistics[3] web site. You will be taken to a search engine where you plug in the parameters of the data you are looking for. Also included on the site is an index to the most popular statistical reports contained on the site. Most general reports can be accessed from this index. This may be a good starting place if you're not sure where to begin.

The Social Statistics Briefing Room[4] is a part of the White House web site. From the main White House site you can link to statistical reports on a number of important social areas. Educational statistics is one of those areas. This is a briefing room – so the reports are not designed to be extensive but rather general summaries on trends and brief reports. For both governmental and nongovernmental statistical reports on education please see the Michigan State University Education Statistics[5] web site. From this site you can access links to all state educational agencies.

To begin making cross-national and cross-cultural comparisons, go to the Higher Education Statistics Agency[6], which has been set up by U.K. universities and higher education colleges to collect, analyze and report on higher education statistics. For a bigger picture on what's going in education try accessing the World Data on Education[7] web site. Here you will be able to see educational profiles and national reports from United Nations member countries where statistical reports on education are available. Most reports are recent; therefore it would be difficult to conduct any sort of longitudinal study with this data. Also included on the site are links to other related world education information sources. World data on education (WDE) focuses on basic descriptions of the main characteristics concerning the organization and functioning of national education systems.

Web Links

1. Department of Education: http://www.ed.gov/
2. Education World: http://www.education-world.com/
3. National Center for Education Statistics: http://nces.ed.gov/pubsearch/
4. Social Statistics Briefing Room:
   http://www.whitehouse.gov/fsbr/education.html
5. Michigan State University Educational Statistics:
   http://www.lib.msu.edu/corby/education/stat.htm
6. Higher Education Statistics Agency: http://www.hesa.ac.uk/
7. World Data on Education:
   http://www.ibe.unesco.org/Inf_Doc/Nat_reps/wdepfome.htm

Politics

For purely biased information about current political events, issues and elections the first places to go are the national political party web sites; Republican National Committee[1] and the Democratic National Committee[2].

The Democratic National Committee

Government News Network[3] The International GovNews Project (GovNews), the result of a collaborative effort in cyberspace between public and private sector volunteers, has completed the groundwork for the wide, cost effective electronic dissemination and discussion of public government information through its creation of a special government "category" on the Internet's Usenet news system. The Project seeks to stimulate open electronic access to public government information and electronic "open democracy" by improving information access and communication by and between governments and between governments and their constituencies. Why not have classes connect to this site and participate in the process?

If you are not familiar with political oriented research material you might want to start at the Online Publications[4] web site. This page is an index of journals and magazines, news resources and publishers of interest to both social and political science. Centre for Research into Elections and Social Trends[5] is a UK site that presents election results and analysis as well as political survey reports from across the UK.

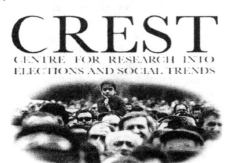

The Harvard-MIT Data Center[6] maintains a large library of electronic data from a number of national sources, a growing collection of unique data sets, and an extensive codebook library. Few other university data centers approach the quantity of social science data that can be accessed from this site. There are over five hundred subsets of data – many related to political issues – that you could use for secondary analysis from this site. At the University of Chicago the Social Research Center[7] maintains the SRC Data Archive is the central repository of data collections used by the social science research community. Its mission is to promote academic research by facilitating the use of primary and secondary research materials. To fulfill this mission the archive acquires and preserves common use resources, provides reference and technical services to researchers, and coordinates storage and use of private/restricted collections.

For a comprehensive collection of information, statistical reports, expert interviews as well as discussion forums on issues related to urban living go to The Urban Institute[8]. Links can be made to political organizations. These should be understood to be important elements of urban organization. The news releases for the media found on the site are a good source of elementary information for introductory level students who are searching for quick facts.

George Modelski at the University of Washington has created a fascinating web page (Evolutionary World Politics Homepage[9]). The site explains itself in this way; *Evolutionary world politics is the employment of evolutionary theory in the study of long-term (structural) transformations in world-wide political arrangements. The subject comprises two main subdivisions: theoretical, and applied. The first concerns the construction, elaboration, and verification of models of structural change in world politics. The second applies this understanding to producing an account of the evolution of world political arrangements, for the past millennium in particular, and to predicting the outlines of such an evolution for the near future.* From this site you can get involved in learning, discussions, debates and link to countless other resources. In the spirit of big picture thinkers like Wallerstein and Mills, Modelski's site conveys the ever-increasing importance of thinking about politics in global ways.

At the online lecture hall you can find Teaching Resources[10] in many disciplines, politics is one. From here you can obtain course syllabi, statistical models and political science lectures. If this area is not one of your strengths, access this site to find supplementary materials for your lectures and presentations. Please refer back to the theory section of this text to find sites related to the philosophy and theory of political behavior.

Web Links

1. Republican National Committee: www.RNC.com
2. Democratic National Committee: www.DNC.com
3. Government News Network: http://www.govnews.org/
4. Online Publications: http://osiris.colorado.edu/POLSCI/RES/pubs.html
5. Centre for Research into Elections and Social Trends: www.ox.ac.uk/
6. Harvard-MIT Data Center: http://hdc-www.harvard.edu/hdc/
7. Social Research Center:
   http://wwwspc.uchicago.edu/DATALIB/datalib.cgi?DIsearch/index
8. The Urban Institute: http://www.urban.org/
9. Evolutionary World Politics Homepage:
   http://faculty.washington.edu/modelski/
10. Teaching Resources:
    http://socsci.Colorado.EDU/POLSCI/RES/teaching.html#s

Marriage and the Family

When trying to understand this most basic of social arrangements one of the first places to look is the U.S. Census. At these sites you can get a quick picture of families. At the US Census Marital Status and Living Arrangements[1] you will find a report by Arlene F. Saluter on current marital status and living arrangements. Check out the US Census Households By Type[2] site and take a look at a chart that breaks down U.S. families by type. These kinds of web pages are great places to use when putting together charts and graphs for assignments and presentations. For a more extensive examination look up The Emerging 21st Century American Family[3] web page. This is a 1999 report by Tom W. Smith who directs the General Social Survey for the National Opinion Research Center. The report analyzes the data from the 1972-98 GSS and suggests a number of important trends. Finally, students might be interested to see the Legal and Economic Benefits of Marriage[4] for a listing of legal benefits that exist for married couples today. You will find some cool facts to add to a report or discussion.

Family Sociology Resources[5] and Family.com[6] are pages oriented more toward consumers (people in families) than they are academic research site. The Family Sociology site does contain a sociology index list and a listing of university marriage and family sociology programs. What's most interesting about sites like these is to see what kind of resources are available out there on the information highway to families – specifically to families who can afford to be online – families who may not be the most likely candidates for these kinds of resources in the first place.

There are a number of private foundations that fund research programs aimed at issues related to children and families. The Kids Count Data and Publications[7] is a project of the Annie E. Casey Foundation, a national and state-by-state effort to track the status of children in the United States. By providing policymakers and citizens with benchmarks of child well being, KIDS COUNT seeks to enrich local, state, and national discussions concerning ways to secure better futures for all children. At the national level, the principal activity of the initiative is the publication of the annual KIDS COUNT Data Book, which uses the best available data to measure the educational, social, economic, and physical well being of children. The Foundation also funds a nationwide network of state-level KIDS COUNT projects that provide a more detailed, community-by-community picture of the condition of children.

A good starting point if you're interested in the classic social problems related to families; poverty, violence, and advocacy is The Family Resources on the Web[8] which links you to sites that are oriented more toward families of lower social class who may not even have access to the internet in their homes. The Australian Institute of Family Studies[9] is a Commonwealth statutory authority established in 1980 to promote the identification and understanding of factors affecting marital and family stability in Australia. See Resources on Domestic Violence[10], a web page with non-linked contact and resource information related to family violence. Cybergrrl Safety Net[11] is a domestic violence website created for women who are in violent relationships. It provides links to useful information and resources, a quiz to determine how knowledgeable you are about domestic violence and an ongoing discussion and forum that you can read and add comments to.

There are a number of faith based family resources out there on the Internet. The Strong Families Network[12] is one that's worth looking into. A majority of families report that religious faith is a central element to their lives. This web site helps to answer questions about how religious organizations are using technology to impact families with education, information and religious teaching. Another such site is the Pure Love Alliance[13]. The mission of the Pure Love Alliance is to educate young people about the benefits of sexual abstinence before marriage and fidelity within marriage. We teach the skills necessary to remain abstinent and to convince others to do the same. We are public advocates for purity and family, vigorously and peacefully opposing individuals and institutions that directly or indirectly promote casual and irresponsible sexual relationships. The site includes topical statistics on teenage sexual behavior and excerpts from recent publications. What's so interesting to sociologists is the phenomenon of the emergence of para-family organizations such this laboring to teach topics that once were the domain of the family alone.

THE STATE OF THE WORLD'S CHILDREN 1996 unicef

The US Department of Health and Human Services' Administration for Children and Families[14] website contains links to government programs related to children and families and a search engine that will enable you to find other government sites that relate to children and families. The Federal government collects all kinds of data and files multitudes of reports. It's a great starting point to find out what the current issues are and what we know so far. A division of the Administration for Children and Families is the Office of Child Support Enforcement. If you'd like to know how your state is doing compared with others in regard to the collection of child support from non-custodial parents go to the State Child Support Enforcement Web Site[15] which also includes a number of non-ACF links that contain relevant information about child-support. Research Forum on Children, Families, and the New Federalism[16] encourages collaborative research and informed policy on welfare reform and child well being. This web site features an on-line database of summaries of large- and small-scale research projects.

There are numbers of web sites out there that contain information related to children. Two important ones are, The Future of Children[17], which contains an index of scientific journals and articles related to children. The State of the World's Children[18] is a web page created by the United Nations Children's Fund (UNICEF: www.unicef.org). The page endeavors to be a global report on the state of the world's children – there's not a whole lot here, yet. The site appears to be a starting place for collecting global information on children. This information is dated 1996, but if you bookmark the page, as it's updated in the future you might be able to keep yourself more current with global children's issues.

We live our lives nested in intimate relationships that both shape and are shaped by us. The Family Relations[19] website contains information about . . .
❑ Relationships, including dating, marriage, and breaking up
❑ Parenting, from pregnancy & dealing with infertility to parenting teenagers
❑ Grandparents and brother/sister relationships
❑ Family problems, including grieving, alcohol & drug use, and divorce
❑ Intimate violence

Although it's not intentionally designed to be so, the Marriage and Family Processes[20] website is a self-contained marriage and family course. The page is an academic sociology site created by Michael C. Kearl at Trinity University (San Antonio). It's part of his larger *Tour Through Cyberspace* that we have previously mentioned. This site could be used as a companion site to your introduction to marriages and families course. There are a number of links that could be incorporated into your course reading list. For students who are considering a specialization in marriage and family studies this should be book-marked and added to your reference collection. The Ohio State University Human Development & Family Life Education Resource Center[21] is another comprehensive site that provides links to all kinds of resources such as educational resources and information technology about marriage and family.

Web Links

1. US Census Marital Status and Living Arrangements:
   http://www.census.gov/population/www/pop-profile/msla.html
2. US Census Households By Type:
   http://www.bls.census.gov/cps/pub/1997/hhldtype.htm
3. The Emerging 21st Century American Family:
   http://www.norc.uchicago.edu/online/emerge.pdf
4. Legal and Economic Benefits of Marriage:
   http://www.religioustolerance.org/mar_bene.htm
5. Family Sociology Resources:
   http://socsci.Colorado.EDU/SOC/RES/family.html
6. Family.com: http://family.go.com/
7. Kids Count Data and Publications:
   http://www.aecf.org/kidscount/index.htm
8. Family Resources on the Web:
   http://web.gc.cuny.edu/dept/socio/resource/family/index.htm
9. Australian Institute of Family Studies: http://www.aifs.org.au/
10. Resources on Domestic Violence:
    http://www.silcom.com/~paladin/madv/astrid.html
11. Cybergrrl Safety Net:
    http://www.cybergrrl.com/fs.jhtml?/views/dv/index.shtml
12. Strong Families Network: www.heavenbound.net/families/
13. Pure Love Alliance: http://purelove.org/top/who.html
14. Administration for Children and Families: http://www.acf.dhhs.gov/
15. State Child Support Enforcement Web Site:
    http://www.acf.dhhs.gov/programs/cse/extinf.htm
16. Research Forum on Children, Families, and the New Federalism:
    http://www.researchforum.org/
17. The Future of Children: http://www.futureofchildren.org/
18. State of the World's Children:
    www.unicef.org/sowc96/contents.htm?477,233
19. Family Relations:
    http://www.personal.psu.edu/faculty/n/x/nxd10/family3.htm
20. Marriage and Family Processes:
    http://www.trinity.edu/~mkearl/family.html
21. Human Development & Family Life Education Resource Center
    www.hec.ohio-state.edu/famlife/index.htm

Medicine and healthcare are becoming important components of an emerging social institution. There are a number of data sites that provide useful scientific information to social researchers. Your local hospital and community health districts are also good places to go to search for reports and statistics on health. See the website for the <u>Harris County Hospital District</u>[1] (the 4th largest in the U.S.) as an example of what might be found in other regions.

At the <u>Centers for Disease Control and Prevention</u>[2] web site you will find links to data and statistics, a health topics index and publications that can be downloaded directly off the site. An interesting link on the site is one that addresses health related hoaxes and rumors. Did you know that there's a rumor out there on the Internet that you can catch necrotizing fasciitis from Costa Rican bananas? Among all the data that you can find at the <u>National Institutes of Health</u>[3] web site, there is a working definition of behavioral and social science research that's possible at the NIH. This standard definition of the field is a good beginning in the effort to chart research territory for sociology of healthcare. <u>The Combined Health Information Database</u>[4] contains information collected by both the NIH and the CDC. In addition to organizing and disseminating research articles, this site also provides you with contact information about the federal agency and scientists involved in collecting comprehensive health information concerning a wide range of health issues and conditions. A collection of research data related to healthcare can be found in the 1998 <u>Greenbook</u>[5]. This site contains a number of reports and papers that are of interest to the social scientist. There are several here that are of special interest to studying healthcare:

- □ National and International Health Care Expenditures and Health Insurance Coverage
- □ Medicare Reimbursement to Hospitals and Physicians
- □ Health Status and Expenditures of the Elderly, and Background Data on Long-Term Care

The Dartmouth Atlas of Health Care

For the past decade, researchers at Dartmouth Medical School's Center for the Evaluative Clinical Sciences have been studying the performance of the health care system in the United States. The results of these studies have been published in the Dartmouth Atlas of Health Care series of publications. You can access these at the <u>Dartmouth Atlas of Healthcare</u>[6]

web site. The Global Health Network[7] (GHNet) is an alliance of experts in health and telecommunications who are actively developing the architecture for a health information structure for the prevention of disease in the 21st century. The professionals involved in GHNet bring together expertise from the essential areas of government, international organizations, business, and academia. All are dedicated individuals, recognized in their fields, who have donated large amounts of time to this project. The GHNet has constructed a distance-learning program in Epidemiology, the Internet and Global Health. The stated goal of the program is to improve health and higher education by using systems technologies that have proven to be effective based upon principles from the Internet culture, cognitive psychology, and quality control in manufacturing. In an attempt to make it available to as many people as possible, the GHNet has constructed a "supercourse" having now 104 lectures. This is an example of a remarkable new development that is occurring all around us in relation to education and healthcare.

Web Links

1. Harris County Hospital District: http://www.tmc.edu/hchd/HCHD.html

2. Centers for Disease Control and Prevention: http://www.cdc.gov/

3. National Institutes of Health: http://www1.od.nih.gov/obssr/def.htm

4. Greenbook: http://aspe.os.dhhs.gov/98gb/toc.htm

5. The Combined Health Information Database: http://chid.nih.gov/

6. Dartmouth Atlas of Healthcare: http://www.dartmouthatlas.org/

7. Global Health Network: http://www.pitt.edu/HOME/GHNet/GHNet.html

Religion

Religion can be one of the most fascinating subjects one can study. The Internet allows us entrée into so many more aspects of this phenomenon. Varieties of global culture have never been more accessible. More data is being collected now than ever before. Organizations and Universities make this information available through newly constructed web pages. The Lilly Foundation is one of the premier funding organizations for religious research in America today. Their American Religion Data Archive[1] represents a collection of quantitative data sets for the study of American religion. Included on the site are surveys of the general population, surveys of religious groups and surveys of religious professionals. In addition to aggregate data files you will find links to other data sets and religious organizations.

To get some idea of comparative church membership numbers go to the 1997 Yearbook of American & Canadian Churches[2] which will provide you with a fact page about membership in religious denominations in North America with 60,000 members or more. There are a number of web sites that can be used as gateways to religious organizations and churches. See the American Studies Web[3] and scroll down past the philosophy links to find dozens of religious sites for religious organizations and specific religious groups. The Religious Movements Homepage[4] is really the granddaddy of religious sites. In addition to dozens of religious group profiles and web links you can connect with a *Sociology of Religious Movements* course resources as well as links to Professor Jeffrey Hadden's Religious Movements, Religious Broadcasting, and Religious Freedom Courses.

To see what many of the current issues in religious studies are these days, access the National Science Foundation: Religion, Democratization, and Market Transition Workshop[5] web page. Here you will find a report from this 1993 workshop, which can be used as a great teaching tool. Another great site for teaching resources is the Max Weber's Sociology of Religion[6] Web page where you can access texts of complete works of Weber's related to religion. The site even has a search engine for words and phrases within Weber's texts.

The American
Religious Experience

If you're interested in more of an historical analysis of religion in this country see the The American Religious Experience[7] web site. This is a course web page developed by Briane Turley at the West Virginia University. The site contains a site-specific search engine, a film archive, articles and links to women in religion, and Religion in American News via Yahoo.com. Also included at this page is a way to access the Journal of Southern Religion. This web page brags that, "classical education is alive and well. Only the medium of communication is changing: chalk dust is giving way to electrons. The Internet furnishes an unprecedented means for collaboration; not only among religion scholars but also between instructors and the students they serve. The new information technologies are more than electronic gadgets; they are powerful tools that can strengthen ties among all members of the academic community. Their potential remains largely untapped in the humanities, but as more scholars venture out onto the information superhighway, we will witness a gradual shift in the way we convey ideas with each other and with our students."

The Princeton University Center for the Study of Religion[8] is a major academic initiative that aims to encourage scholarly research, teaching, and public discussion about religion through the diverse perspectives of the humanities and social sciences. This site addresses a wide variety of religious experience. The researcher will be exposed to a full-blown program in religious studies at Princeton.

The Institute for the Study of American Religion[9] sponsors another great site that concentrates on religion in America where you can find information about local religious cults and sects. See also the Apologetics Index[10] for research resources on cults, sects, movements, and religious doctrines. From this page you can access news reports, definitions, terms and book reviews. Terry Matthews at Wake Forest University focuses on the Southern religious experience at his site Lectures on Southern Religion[11]. The purpose of theTelevangelism[12] site it to provide a gateway to access the massive amount of material of the internet about religious broadcasting. Almost every televangelist, many radio broadcasters, and many parachurch organizations that utilize broadcasting now have Web sites. This page provides a set of links, with abstracts, that will permit you to access all of these sites. This web site also presents a bibliography of significant writings about religious broadcasting. In addition, many of the writings of the author have been archived here for easy access.

An important religious resource both here in America and worldwide is the Catholic Church. The New Advent: Catholic Resources Online[13] web page provides an online Catholic encyclopedia, links to the Vatican, Catholic Church teachings, practices and an index that references the Bible. While this site is not designed for social research – it's for religious consumers to learn about the Catholic faith – it holds volumes of valuable information about the world's largest religious group.

There are several sites that address a number of specific religious groups. www.Zipple.com[14] is a Jewish super-site containing news, information, travel, cultural experiences, a site specific search engine, even a dating service (for when you get tired of working on that research project all alone). See also the Jewish Online Student Research Center[15] for more information about Judaism, anti-Semitism, and the Holocaust.

The Islam World Net[16] has an online search engine of the holy texts in the Muslim faith, links to sites that explain the religion to non-Muslims, explanations of fundamental beliefs, prophecies, prayers, books, texts, and theology. This is an enormous site. It's an essential starting place for any serious study of the Islamic faith. Go to the Native American Spirituality[17] web page an explore links from religious movements homepages and native American religion web sites. To understand the religious landscape of this country study The Church of Jesus Christ of Latter Day Saints[18] web page where you can also access The Book of Mormon[19] (online) to read for yourself the doctrines and beliefs of this uniquely American religion.

New Religious Movements[20] page contains a diverse collection of spiritual and social worldviews. All the groups present on this site should be treated separately and are included together here only for convenience and no value judgment is implied. What I find most interesting is the popular response, both within organized religion and within mainstream media, to alternative spirituality than in any theological justification for their existence. To end your study of religion on the internet you'll need to visit the Links to Revelation, Apocalyptic and Millennial Websites and Materials[21] to see texts and commentaries as well as introductory materials, books and articles. There's even a way for you to visit academic and on-line classes.

Web Links

1. American Religion Data Archive: http://www.arda.tm/

2. 1997 Yearbook of American & Canadian Churches:
   http://www.dnaco.net/~kbedell/ybstats2.htm

3. American Studies Web:
   http://www.georgetown.edu/crossroads/asw/philos.html

4. Religious Movements Homepage:
   http://cti.itc.virginia.edu/~jkh8x/soc257/

5. National Science Foundation: Religion, Democratization, and Market
   Transition Workshop: http://www.nsf.gov/sbe/ses/sociol/works3.htm

6. Max Weber's Sociology of Religion:
   http://4sociology.4anything.com/network-frame/0,1855,6401-
   62110,00.html

7. The American Religious Experience: http://are.as.wvu.edu/

8. Princeton University Center for the Study of Religion:
   http://www.princeton.edu/~csrelig/

9. Institute for the Study of American Religion:
   http://www.americanreligion.org/index.html

10. Apologetics Index: http://www.gospelcom.net/apologeticsindex/

11. Lectures on Southern Religion:
    http://www.wfu.edu:/~matthetl/south/lectures.html

12. Televangelism: http://cti.itc.virginia.edu/~jkh8x/tvrel/tvrelhome.htm

13. New Advent: Catholic Resources Online: http://www.newadvent.org/

14. www.Zipple.com

15. Jewish Online Student Research Center:
    http://www.us-israel.org/jsource/

16. The Islam World Net: http://www.islamworld.net/

17. Native American Spirituality:
    http://cti.itc.virginia.edu/~jkh8x/soc257/nrms/naspirit.html

18. The Church of Jesus Christ of Latter Day Saints: http://www.lds.org/

19. The Book of Mormon (online):
    http://www.hti.umich.edu/m/mormon//browse.html

20. New Religious Movements: http://www.academicinfo.net/nrms.html

21. Links to Revelation, Apocalyptic and Millennial Websites and Materials:
    http://clawww.lmu.edu/faculty/fjust/Apocalyptic_Links.htm

Gender and Women's Studies

Web sites under this section are divided into several general categories: Gender Studies, Resource sites, politically oriented pages and Men's Studies. A good starting point is the Women's and Gender Studies Database on the Internet[1], which is a German site that has an English translation. Check out the Gender Inn which is a searchable database providing access to over 6000 records pertaining to feminist theory, feminist literary criticism and gender studies focusing on English and American literature. These pages also include a site-specific search engine to help you find information.

The Women's Studies/Resources Research Sites[2] is a selective, annotated, highly acclaimed listing of web sites containing resources and information about women's studies / women's issues, with an emphasis on sites of particular use to an academic women's studies program. From these pages you can access over 500 articles focusing on gender studies. For an incredibly extensive array of links go to the Feminism and Women's Studies[3] web site. This page will connect you to a very comprehensive collection of web links:

- Activism
- Gender & Sexuality
- Women's Health
- The Workplace
- Women's History
- Academic Discourse
- Women's Studies
- Other Links

The American Studies Web[4] has a number of links to sites to help you research sociology. The women's studies resources is an index to specific sites ranging from history-related, current events, issues oriented, women's hall of fame, and global news related to women. The Feminist Theory Website[5] provides research materials and information for students, activists, and scholars interested in women's conditions and struggles around the world. The goals of this website are: 1) to encourage a wide range of research into feminist theory, and 2) to encourage dialogue between women (and men) from different countries around the world. Hopefully, this will result in new connections, new ideas, and new information about feminist theory and women's movements. The site focuses on three subsections 1) various fields within feminist theory; 2) different national / ethnic feminisms; and 3) individual feminists.

Again, Professor Kearl at Trinity University has provided us with a fantastic gender web site. His Gender and Society[6]: Contains web links that are integrated into the text of a summary presentation about gender. This is a very user-friendly site and seemingly oriented to students who are just learning the essential topics related to gender. The website represents a whole seminar on gender with web links on topics such as income, power, historical and cross-cultural sites incorporated. A specific site that uses gender concepts to focus the researcher on issues such as world peace and the nature of humanity is the Jane Addams Biography and Quotes[7] web page.

WomenWatch

The UN Internet Gateway for Women's Studies[8] is an international site that focuses on the advancement and empowerment of women. This is more of a politically biased site but it still contains much useful information specifically related to the Beijing Conference on Women. The page is concerned with providing updated information on the aftermath of the conference, global UN efforts related to women's issues and fostering communication among people interested in women's issues. The Women in Politics Database[9] is another politically oriented site. It contains a bibliographic database of articles related to women in politics, organized by the Inter-Parliamentary Union. The IPU is the world organization of parliaments of sovereign states. It was established in 1889. The Union is the focal point for worldwide parliamentary dialogue and works for peace and co-operation among peoples and for the firm establishment of representative democracy.

The Feminist Majority Foundation Online[10] web page advertises itself as, "…committed to empowering women and winning equality through research, the sharing of information of value to feminists everywhere, and effective action." It's a site designed for women but I'm sure they wouldn't mind if interested researchers surfed through. The site's News and Press Release selection offers to keep visitors up to date with breaking developments affecting women. The Feminist Events Calendar will enable you to select by date, or conduct a search by topic or geographic location for those events of interest to you. Another comprehensive resource site is the Feminism and Women's Resources.[11] This is a listing of many feminism, women's studies, or women-related sources on the net.

The American Men's Studies Association[12] is a not for profit professional organization of scholars, therapists, and others interested in the exploration of masculinity in modern society. As the members and supporters of the Men's Studies movement forward their suggestions, they will be considered for incorporation in this page. The site includes links, resources, men's study courses, and a journal. Menstuff National Men's Resource[13] has thousands of men's resources and hyperlinks, hundreds of men's issues, events, periodicals and groups and thousands of on-site men's book reviews & covers. The site boasts about being an educational nonprofit volunteer web site that serves a diverse men's community (men's rights, mythopoetic, pro-feminist, recovery, re-evaluation counseling, and religious). This web page provides information on over 100 men's issues regarding positive change in male roles and relationships (including abuse, aging, circumcision, divorce, fathers, health, isolation, kid stuff, mid-life, multicultural, prostate, sexuality, spirituality, transition, violence, work, etc.).

Finally, for a host of useful facts and figures on the economic aspect of gender arrangements in this country, surf to the Earning Differences Between Men and Women[14] web page. The site is sponsored by the US Department of Labor Women's Bureau. Obviously, you will find statistical report on earnings differences between men and women, but there are also graphic presentations which can be copied and incorporated into presentations and papers. The web site includes bibliography for further reading and research.

Web Links

1. Women's and Gender Studies Database on the Internet:
   http://www.uni-koeln.de/phil-fak/englisch/datenbank/e_index.htm

2. UN Internet Gateway for Women's Studies :www.un.org/womenwatch

3. Women's Studies/Resources Research Sites:
   http://www.unix.umbc.edu/~korenman/wmst/links.html

4. Feminism and Women's Studies:
   http://eserver.org/feminism/index.html

5. American Studies Web:
   http://www.georgetown.edu/crossroads/asw/wmst.html

6. Feminist Theory Website :www.cddc.vt.edu/feminism/

7. Gender and Society: http://www.trinity.edu/mkearl/gender.html

8. Jane Addams Biography and Quotes:
   http://4sociology.4anything.com/network-frame/0,1855,6401-
   61283,00.html

9. Women in Politics Database :http://www.ipu.org/bdf-e/BDFsearch.asp

10. Feminist Majority Foundation Online:www.feminist.org

11. Feminism and Women's Resources:
    http://www3.50megs.com/jmansfield//feminism/index.html

12. American Men's Studies Association:
    http://members.aol.com/amsapage/

13. Menstuff National Mens Resource:http://www.menstuff.org/

14. Earning Differences Between Men and Women:
    http://www.dol.gov/dol/wb/public/wb_pubs/wagegap2.htm

SOCIAL INEQUALITY

Social Class

To begin calculating social characteristics related to social class such as socioeconomic status, the first place to go is the U.S. Census Bureau Income Statistics[1]. Like all other such pages maintained by the Census Bureau the Income Statistics site and the U.S. Census Bureau Poverty Statistics[2] both contain the latest and most accurate statistics available. On these pages you will find longitudinal reports, statistical reports on income by population, median income reports, and federal definitions of poverty. Look also at the 1998 Greenbook[3], which contains references to some income data, also statistics regarding Social Security, Supplemental Security Income, Unemployment compensation, and Welfare (AFDC) figures. Other useful statistics that you can find on this site include tax provisions related to retirement, health, poverty, employment, disability and other social Issues.

Another site by professor Kearl at Trinity University, Explorations in social inequality[4] is designed as a self-contained seminar on the topic with dozens of web links integrated into the presentation. Many of the web pages in the Tour Through Cyberspace gateway site have been designed as stand alone tours through the essential categories in the field. This site is no different. It's a great place for beginners, yet has a depth of coverage unlike other sites in this category. A related web page seeks to answer the important question, Why the Poor are Poor[5]. Here you will find an excellent presentation on the social psychology of poverty. The National Coalition for the Homeless[6] web page is an advocacy site concentrating on issues related to poverty and homelessness. From the site you can access resource directories, a fact sheet about homelessness, an online library and links to related publications.

The Internet has several great sources for lectures and presentations related to social class. Inequality.org[7] is a journalism oriented web page about inequality in income, wealth and health. The site is a gold mine of information that could be used as a companion web site for courses on social class. It would be important to point out that journalism isn't science. Lecturesonline.org[8] will link you to dozens of papers and course lectures related to issues in social inequality. Topics include; home ownership by race, the black middle class, and the earning ladder. For a global perspective on the subject go to <u>SocioSite's social inequality and stratification resources</u>[9]. The SocioSite is another gateway to hundreds of resources in sociology. From this page you can find links to papers, reports, and statistics on issues related to inequality from all over the world. The site is especially strong in the areas of poverty and social class. Also included on this site is a section with teaching strategies. Look at the 30-hour famine project as a very creative hand's on teaching method.

The Multidisciplinary Program in Inequality & Social Policy at Harvard University emerged from the conviction that certain research puzzles may be particularly suited to an interdisciplinary approach. The program's web site, <u>Harvard University's Inequality and Social Policy Web Site Think Tank Links</u>[10] has information that is oriented toward scholars from a variety of fields. Great comparisons among social classes can be made when you go to the <u>American Heritage's ranking of the wealthiest American's of all time</u>[11] where there are biographical links to the 40 members of this list. Thorstein Veblen's classic text on the emerging modern class structure in America can now be found at <u>Veblen's Theory of the Leisure Class</u>[12]. Because the text is in word processing format you can transfer sections of his work into papers and presentations. Veblen's concept of conspicuous consumption seems to ring true with students these days.

As a foil to the Veblen text you can import graphic images from <u>The Austin Chronicles Hypermedia Gallery on Homeless Teenagers</u>[13] into your papers and presentations. Photojournalist Jana Birchum spent 6 weeks in January and February 1995, chronicling the lives of young homeless living on the streets of Austin, Texas. Her dramatic photographs were first presented in the March 24, 1995 edition of The Austin Chronicle. Add some more important facts to your visual presentation by going to the <u>Homelessness in America</u>[14] web page and find information about:

❑ The New Poverty	❑ Pregnant & Homeless
❑ About The Homeless	❑ Children
❑ How Many?	❑ Poverty Nomads
❑ Families with Children	❑ Family Myth
❑ Men	❑ Veterans

Web Links

1. U.S. Census Bureau Income Statistics:
   http://www.census.gov/ftp/pub/hhes/www/income.html
2. U.S. Census Bureau Poverty Statistics:
   http://www.census.gov/ftp/pub/hhes/www/poverty.html
3. 1998 Greenbook: http://aspe.os.dhhs.gov/98gb/toc.htm
4. Explorations in social inequality http://www.trinity.edu/mkearl/strat.html
5. Why the Poor are Poor: http://www.trinity.edu/mkearl/socpsy-8.html#wp
6. Inequality.org: http://www.inequality.org/
7. Lecturesonline.org:
   http://www.lectureonline.org/social_sciences/sociology.htm
8. SocioSite's social inequality and stratification resources:
   http://www.pscw.uva.nl/sociosite/TOPICS/Inequality.html\
9. Harvard University's Inequality and Social Policy Web Site Think Tank
   Links:
   http://www.ksg.harvard.edu/inequality/Focus/links.htm
10. American Heritage's ranking of the wealthiest American's of all time:
    http://www.americanheritage.com/98/oct/40index.htm
11. Veblen's Theory of the Leisure Class:
    http://socserv2.socsci.mcmaster.ca/~econ/ugcm/3ll3/veblen/leisure/index.html
12. National Coalition for the Homeless: http://nch.ari.net/
13. The Austin Chronicles Hypermedia Gallery on Homeless Teenagers:
    http://www.auschron.com/gallery/
14. Homelessness in America:
    http://www.qvctc.commnet.edu/student/GaryOKeefe/homeless/frame.ht
    ml

Race & Ethnicity

Closely tied to studies of social class are those concerned with race and ethnicity. Research in these areas focus on the relationship between these variables and others such as social class, education, political affiliation and religiosity (to name just a few broad categories). If you haven't already been to professor Kearl's Tour Through Cybersociety you've missed an incredible Internet experience. Within the site he has created a number of subject specific course pages. I refer to these as "course pages" because they are a self-contained curricula. His Race and Ethnicity[1] page is the first stop on this particular tour. There are dozens and dozens of links to related sites about a variety of racial and ethnic categories containing statistical information as well as stories, texts and theories.

Another returning web gateway is the American Studies Web[2] with links to several important sites such as the Minority Affairs Forum, Race and Ethnicity Book Reviews, and Immigration Resources. More specific web searches can be made from the African American Internet Links[3]. In addition to online resources, listservs, search engines and newsgroups you can find links to academic programs of study. Similar sites (all sponsored by UCLA) are the Latino Internet Sites[4] and the Asian American Sites[5]. Another university site is the Race and Ethnic Studies Institute[6] at Texas A&M. The Institute's self described mission is to conduct and disseminate--at regional, national, and international levels--interdisciplinary and policy research pertaining to race and ethnicity across various public policy areas.

The Virtual Library on Migration and Ethnic Relations[7] is the oldest catalog of the web, started by Tim Berners-Lee, the creator of html and the web itself. Unlike commercial catalogs, it is run by a loose confederation of volunteers, who compile pages of key links for particular areas in which they are expert; even though it isn't the biggest index of the web, the VL pages are widely recognized as being among the highest-quality guides to particular sections of the web. This site includes links to media, resources, organizations, and research programs. Also included is a search engine to search by topic or keyword. The Race and Ethnicity Collection[8] is one of over forty literary collections on the Eserver and consists of reference material, essays, and other works addressing issues of race and ethnicity in the United States. It also includes a search engine for the site. The site-specific search engines are helpful when you know what you're looking for and don't want to waste time hunting.

Several more specific web pages, while often politically biased, still contain much useful information – you'll just have to weed through it more carefully. The Origins of Affirmative Action[9] will give you a history of this social policy and several links to historical references. Going to The Arayan Nations Web Site[10] will enable you to find out what hate groups like this have to say about themselves. When you get to this site you find interesting the blending of religion with racial and ethnic enmity. For the "total Black web experience" try visiting the African American Web Connection[11]. This web page promises to be an Afro-centric cultural journey. Visiting this and similar sites is highly recommended for students who have had limited contact with people from other racial and ethnic backgrounds.

The Hoover Institute[12] is a think tank at Stanford University. One of this organization's leading scholars is Thomas Sowell who has written a number of influential books related to race and ethnicity including *Race, Culture and Equality*. In his remarks at the Commonwealth Club of California on June 18, 1998, Thomas Sowell discussed the conclusions he reached after spending fifteen years researching the economic and social impacts of cultural differences among peoples and nations around the world. This essay, Race, Culture, and Equality, distills the results found in the trilogy that was published during these years---*Race and Culture* (1994), *Migrations and Cultures* (1996), and *Conquests and Cultures* (1998). The purpose of the Institution is to promote peace. Its records stand as a challenge to those who promote war (About the Hoover Institution)[13].

Web Links

1. Race and Ethnicity http://www.trinity.edu/mkearl/race.html
2. American Studies Web:
   http://www.georgetown.edu/crossroads/asw/genethnic.html
3. African American Internet Links:
   http://latino.sscnet.ucla.edu/Afro.links.html
4. Latino Internet Sites: http://latino.sscnet.ucla.edu/latinos.links.html
5. Asian American Sites: http://latino.sscnet.ucla.edu/Asian.links.html
6. **Race and Ethnic Studies Institute**: http://resi.tamu.edu/index.html
7. Virtual Library on Migration and Ethnic Relations:
   http://www.ercomer.org/wwwvl/
8. The Race and Ethnicity Collection: http://eserver.org/race/
9. The Origins of Affirmative Action: http://www.now.org/nnt/08-
   95/affirmhs.html
10. The Arayan Nations Web Site: http://www.christian-aryannations.com/
11. African American Web Connection: http://www.aawc.com/aawc0.html
12. The Hoover Institute:
    http://www-hoover.stanford.edu/publications/he/23/23a.html
13. About the Hoover Institution:
    http://www-hoover.stanford.edu/main/whatis.html

Social Control And Deviance

Web pages in this section cover a broad range of topics and theories including deviant behavior, crime, social control, prisons, criminology, and juvenile delinquency. The best pages in this category are from government agencies such as the FBI, White House, Department of Justice, and Bureau of Justice Statistics.

The Inter-university Consortium for Political and Social Research maintains a web site containing the National Archive for Criminal Justice Data[1]. Established in 1978 under the auspices of ICPSR and the Bureau of Justice Statistics (BJS), U.S. Department of Justice, the NACJD currently holds over 500 data collections relating to criminal justice. This website provides browsing and downloading access to most of this data and documentation. The U.S. Dept of Justice, Bureau of Justice Statistics[2] is an essential resource site for students and researchers focused on criminology. The page has an indexed catalog of all BJS publications. There are several versions of each article you can download as well as order hard copies. Most articles are written using data collections – data sets and codebooks can also be ordered off this site.

If you backtrack to the Bureau of Justice Statistics Homepage[3] you will more extensive links to publications, data, information, and datasets related to crime, juvenile justice, and State contacts. This extensive site also contains a BJS publications order form, information about other products available from the BJS Clearinghouse, links to World Wide Web (WWW) Sites, State World Wide Web (WWW) Sites, File Transfer Protocol (FTP) Sites and Listservs. This is a statistics site sponsored by the federal government. From this page you can access these other important sources of information for researching crime:

- ❑ Crime and Victims Statistics, Bureau of Justice Statistics[4]
- ❑ Statistics on Drugs and Crime, Bureau of Justice Statistics[5]
- ❑ Information Products from the Bureau of Justice Statistics Clearinghouse[6]
- ❑ International Justice Statistics, Bureau of Justice Statistics[7]

There are a significant number of important government supported web pages related to reporting information about crime. The Social Statistics Briefing Room[8] is a part of the White House web site. From this site you can link to statistical reports on a number of important social areas. Crime statistics is one of those areas. This is a briefing room – so the reports are not designed to be extensive but more general, targeting trends and summaries.

Would you like to know the latest data on drug abuse in the U.S.? The DEA Homepage[9] provides up-to-date statistics regarding arrests, drug lab seizures, drug removal efforts, and drug testing. The page links you to another site that gives pharmacological and usage data about "drugs of concern" to the DEA. Also on the web page are links to information about law enforcement efforts by the agency (budget/staffing, training and agent deaths). Also included are links to ten key publications such as; legalization issues, intelligence reports and press releases.

The Federal Bureau of Investigation has a similar web page that's filled with data and major links to crime related sites. From The FBI Homepage[10] you will be able to access the FBI Uniform Crime Reports.[11] All sociology students are all exposed to the UCR. It's one thing to read about the information contained in these kinds of reports, it can be a whole other ball game for students to actually see the report, explore it on their own and make their own comparisons. This can take learning to another level. Go to the Federal Bureau of Prisons[12] web site, a page that calls itself a source of quick facts related to prisons, prisoners, and employees of the Bureau of Prisons. After you visit some of these government sites you will undoubtedly be convinced that we are in the information age. An excellent summary page for all the statistical reports you can find on government pages is the Federal Crime Statistics Organizational Index.[13] What this page will do is assist in your understanding of how all the Federal crime statistics sites on the web are related. There are, of course, many more Federal sites on the web, but I have listed only those offering crime statistics on their sites.

The National Criminal Justice Reference Service[14] (NCJRS) is one of the most extensive sources of information on criminal and juvenile justice in the world, providing services to an international community of policymakers and professionals. NCJRS is a collection of clearinghouses supporting all bureaus of the U.S. Department of Justice, Office of Justice Programs: the National Institute of Justice, the Office of Juvenile Justice and Delinquency Prevention, the Bureau of Justice Statistics, the Bureau of Justice Assistance, the Office for Victims of Crime, and the OJP Program Offices. It also supports the Office of National Drug Control Policy. Criminal Justice Statistics[15] is the link that offers online full-text publications available on the NCJRS website and on partner agency websites listed alphabetically. If you know the title of the publication you are seeking, start here.

The Legal Information Institute offers <u>Supreme Court</u>[16] opinions under the auspices of Project Hermes, the court's electronic-dissemination project. This archive contains nearly all opinions of the court issued since May of 1990. In addition, the page offers a collection of over 600 of the most important historical decisions of the Court is available on CD-ROM and (with reduced functionality) over the Net.

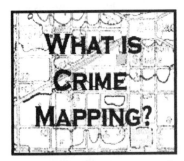

In order to conduct a spatial analysis of crime you'll need to access meaningful maps of urban centers. The National Institute of Justice sponsors the <u>Crime Mapping Research Center</u>.[17] Established in 1997, the goal of the Center is the promotion, research, evaluation, development, and dissemination of GIS (geographic information systems) technology and the spatial analysis of crime.

The <u>Office of Juvenile Justice and Delinquency Prevention</u>[18] web site is designed to provide information and resources on both general areas of interest about juvenile justice and delinquency including conferences, funding opportunities, and new publications and the comprehensive strategy as a framework for communities to combat youth crime. There are a number of major categories of information on this site, they include:

❑ **Topical Resources.** Provides resources on a variety of timely and specific topics - such as gangs, gun violence, and school violence.

- **National and International Organizations and Agencies**. Provides contact information and links for organizations and agencies across the country and around the world that focus on youth. You may search by topical area or by alphabet.

- **State Resources**. Provides State-by-State lists of contacts, including Juvenile Justice Specialists, State Advisory Groups, Missing Children, Clearinghouses, and Departments of Juvenile Justice, Education, and Sheriff's Associations. The site allows you to search by State or type of contact.

- **Teleconference Series**. OJJDP's Satellite Teleconference series offers a convenient and cost-effective method of providing information to diverse juvenile justice constituencies all over the country. Videotapes of past broadcasts are available for purchase.

I've already written about the Sociology Online site, it's a UK academic gateway to a number of our specialized subject areas. Sociology Online: Criminology[19] in addition to links and resources also contains access to lecture notes, Power Point slide shows that focus on crime statistics. Reports and documents related to many of the legal aspects of crime and punishment can be accessed off the ACLU Criminal Justice Page.[20] The page will provide you with accessibility to legal advice and court case archives. You will be able to link to other criminal justice sites and reference articles and case studies as well as see a list of books of interest. The web page includes a site-specific search engine.

Web Links

1. National Archive for Criminal Justice Data:
   http://www.icpsr.umich.edu/NACJD/

2. U.S. Dept of Justice, Bureau of Justice Statistics:
   http://www.ojp.usdoj.gov/bjs/pubalp2.htm

3. Bureau of Justice Statistics Homepage:
   http://www.ojp.usdoj.gov/bjs/welcome.html

4. Crime and Victims Statistics, Bureau of Justice Statistics:
   http://www.ojp.usdoj.gov/bjs/cvict.htm

5. Statistics on Drugs and Crime, Bureau of Justice Statistics:
   http://www.ojp.usdoj.gov/bjs/drugs.htm

6. Information Products from the Bureau of Justice Statistics
   Clearinghouse: http://www.ncjrs.org/statprdt.htm

7. International Justice Statistics, Bureau of Justice Statistics:
   http://www.ojp.usdoj.gov/bjs/ijs.htm

8. Social Statistics Briefing Room:
   http://www.whitehouse.gov/fsbr/crime.html

9. The DEA Homepage: http://www.usdoj.gov/dea/

10. The FBI Homepage: http://www.fbi.gov/homepage.htm

11. FBI Uniform Crime Reports: http://www.fbi.gov/ucr.htm

12. Federal Bureau of Prisons: http://www.bop.gov/fact0598.html

13. Federal Crime Statistics Organizational Index: http://www.crime.org/fed-index.html

14. National Criminal Justice Reference Service: http://www.ncjrs.org/

15. Criminal Justice Statistics: http://www.ncjrs.org/statwww.htm

16. Supreme Court Decisions: http://supct.law.cornell.edu:8080/supct/

17. Crime Mapping Research Center: http://www.ojp.usdoj.gov/cmrc/

18. Office of Juvenile Justice and Delinquency Prevention:
    http://ojjdp.ncjrs.org/

19. Sociology Online: Criminology
    http://www.sociologyonline.f9.co.uk/SubjectAreasNNCrime.htm

20. ACLU Criminal Justice Page:
    http://www.aclu.org:80/issues/criminal/hmcj.html

SOCIAL DYNAMICS & SOCIAL CHANGE

Social Movements, Demography and Globalization

When we speak of social dynamics we refer to the ways that society changes. These dynamic changes that society undergoes take many forms. One of the most basic of dynamics that societies experience is the demographic change in their populations due to births, deaths, and migration. Globalization speaks of phenomena related to modernization, technology and economic development.

To begin your search for information related to social movements you should start at the American Sociological Association Section on Collective Behavior and Social Movements.[1] *The purpose of the CBSM section is to foster the study of emergent and extra-institutional social forms and behavior, particularly crowds and social movements. This includes but is not limited to disasters, riots, protest, rumors, panics, fads, fashions, popular culture, strikes, and reform, revival and revolutionary movements.* This web page includes papers, meeting notices, and links to teaching resources related to the subject. One useful link from this site is one that will take you to Social Activism Sites on the Web[2] where you can access dozens of specialized web pages describing a variety of dynamic social behavior. There's a wonderful paper on the internet, Narratives of Possibility: Social Movements, Collective Stories, and the Dilemmas of Practice,[3] *it uses narrative, with its power to bring meaning to the otherwise random assaults of daily life, as a conceptual entry point into the practices through which people make choices, shape action, and create social movements.* This paper is one of many resources that can be found on the New Social Movement Network.[4] Go to the documents section to find a number of academic papers on the general topic of social movements.

Read the online paper Computer Linked Social Movements[5] to become more familiar with some of the issues being addressed and how technology is related to social change. The culture of social movements in the history of America can be researched from the Social Movement Cultures[6] web site. This site is under development but contains some useful bibliographies and online course materials. The focus of this site is the practices and processes of social movements, including rituals and symbolically charged actions, idiolects and jargons, works of art, unique value systems, and a variety of other elements. The general aim of this web page is to help in the study of social movements, defined as ... *all those practices and meaning-making processes by which those within a given movement express their distinctiveness vis-à-vis the surrounding culture(s) with which they interact.*

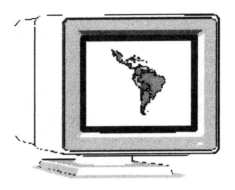

For a trip through one of our previously mentioned sociology gateways go to the SocioSite and access the Special Forms of Activism and Social Movements[7] for dozens of links to web pages from several other cultures. Social movements are trans-cultural. There are a number of web pages that will take you to the variety that exists in social movement data. Latin American Social Movements on the WWW[8] includes starting points related Latin American studies, organizations, funding agencies, and national sites. On the Women and Social Movements in the United States[9] web page you will find projects that link you to position papers on a variety of historical topics related to women's social activism. To access a list of online information storage sites (FTP, Gopher, Telnet, WWW, databases and bulletin boards) go to the Black/African Related Resources[10] web page. This page and it's related connections contain a significant amount of information relating to or of concern to Black or African people, culture, and issues around the world, either in files or conferences. Also included (in other sections of the list) are resources relating to ethnic/intercultural relations, international/sustainable development (includes global networking), and social/progressive activism.

The textbook publisher Allyn and Bacon has a comprehensive internet site on Collective Behavior and Social Movements[11] from which you can access any number of social movement web pages directly. The site has a general category and then specifically organizes other links into abortion, censorship, guns/militias, and peace/democracy categories. www.Cybersociology.com[12] is a non-profit multi-disciplinary webzine dedicated to the critical discussion of the internet, cyberspace, cyberculture and life online. From this site you can access the Grassroots Political Activism Online[13], which is a page in this webzine containing web links to a growing number of smaller politically oriented social change advocacy sites.

There are a number of important web sites that you will need to visit if you are interested in demographic research. First among them is the Statistical Abstract of the U.S.[14] The files contained on this site are in a PDF format. You can learn about health, natural resources, income and foreign commerce to name just a few of the files available from this comprehensive site. For information targeted more at populations, go to the Current Population Survey where you will be able to view any number of surveys related data. *The CPS is the primary source of information on the labor force characteristics of the U.S. population. Each month a sample is selected to represent the civilian non-institutional population. Respondents are interviewed to obtain information about the employment status of each member of the household 15 years of age and older. However, published data focus on those ages 16 and over. The sample provides estimates for the nation as a whole and serves as part of model-based estimates for individual states and other geographic areas.* There are a number of topical reports that can be downloaded from the site as well. These reports range in topic from labor, employment, race, poverty, and school enrollment.

For a more basic presentation of demographic data you should access the Missouri State Data Center at Basic US Census Data Tables[15] to see a number of general charts, graphs and tables reflecting statistical data about the U.S. 1990 census. The data is presented by state, county, city/places and metropolitan areas. It is also possible to access a number of government reports on population from this site. You will also find a number of graphic representations you can download for presentations. Look for updates when the 2000 census is ready.

What better place to start when wanting to know what's going on in the American culture. Sociology students will find The Gallup Organization[16] to be a great jumping off point for writing papers and making presentations about a variety of social dynamics: elections, business and the economy, social issues, and lifestyle choices. Link this website to your course website. Take a look at the CIA World Fact Book[17] for not so covert information from the Central Intelligence Agency about global trends. At this site, the CIA provides profiles for every country in the world. Access the Social Statistics Briefing Room[18] sponsored by the White House and see brief summaries of important social statistics related to world population, income, poverty and home ownership.

PRB SEARCH   QUICKFACTS PUBLICATIONS ABOUT PRB ORDER

POPULATION REFERENCE BUREAU
...providing timely and objective population information

The Population Reference Bureau[19] is the leader in providing timely and objective information on U.S. and international population trends and their implications. PRB informs policymakers, educators, the media, and concerned citizens working in the public interest around the world through a broad range of activities, including publications, information services, seminars and workshops, and technical support. PRB also produces specialized publications covering population and public policy issues in the United States and in other countries (see publications catalog, or go to Regions Map on PRB's Home Page for links to publications about specific world regions or countries). PRB publishes the Population Today newsletter, the quarterly Population Bulletin, the annual World Population Data Sheet, and PRB Reports on America. You can use information from this site to create customized demographic tables. The large body of data contained in this site is made more accessible using a site specific search engine.

The U.S. Demography Homepage[20] is part of an initiative to identify, document, and provide simple access to demographic information concerning The United States of America. This part describes CIESIN's data holdings and related information. This HomePage consists of a series of cascading hypertext links providing access to national data resources, on-line supporting documentation (codebooks, data dictionaries, citations), and possibly extraction tools for data access, and you may connect to an anonymous FTP service for data file retrieval.

The Population Index on the Web[21] published since 1935, is the primary reference tool to the world's population literature. It presents an annotated bibliography of recently published books, journal articles, working papers, and other materials on population topics. The Index is provided free of charge on the Web as a public service, thanks to financial support from NICHD. Population Index on the Web is a joint project of Population Index and the Computing and Library Cores at the Office of Population Research, Princeton University. Part of the World Wide Web Virtual Library, The Internet Guide to Demography and Population Studies[22] is an Australian site that links you to a variety of sources of information on the internet about populations and the study of demography. It contains a search engine in which you type in the topic you are interested in studying.

To begin your study of globalization, take a look at the Development, Social Transformation and Globalisation[23] (need to use Adobe Acrobat) where you will access a paper written by Stephen Castles director of The Centre for Asia Pacific Social Transformation Studies. In the paper he suggests new and more useful ways of looking at globalization as a form of

94

world transformation and development. Another paper that you should read from the Internet is located at <u>World Social Situation</u>[24] by Richard J. Estes, Ph.D. of the University of Pennsylvania. In this paper and accompanying figures and tables Estes presents a comprehensive survey of worldwide social development trends for the 25-year period spanning 1970-1995.

Web Links

1. ASA Section on Collective Behavior and Social Movements:
   http://www.u.arizona.edu/~jearl/cbsm.html
2. Social Activism Sites on the Web:
   http://www.u.arizona.edu/~jearl/active.htm
3. Narratives of Possibility: Social Movements, Collective Stories, and the
   Dilemmas of Practice: http://www.interweb-
   tech.com/nsmnet/docs/kling.htm
4. New Social Movement Network: http://www.interweb-tech.com/nsmnet/
5. Computer Linked Social Movements:
   http://www.eco.utexas.edu/faculty/Cleaver/polnet.html
6. Social Movement Cultures: http://www.wsu.edu:8080/~amerstu/smc/
7. SocioSite Special Forms of Activism and Social Movements:
   http://www.pscw.uva.nl/sociosite/TOPICS/Activism.html#SPECIAL
8. Latin American Social Movements on the WWW:
   http://www.ncl.ac.uk/library/guides/lasmig.html
9. Women and Social Movements in the United States:
   http://womhist.binghamton.edu/
10. Black/African Related Resources:
    http://www.sas.upenn.edu/African_Studies/Home_Page/mcgee.html
11. Collective Behavior and Social Movements:
    http://www.abacon.com/sociology/soclinks/collect.html
12. www.Cybersociology.com
13. Grassroots Political Activism Online:
    http://www.socio.demon.co.uk/magazine/5/issue5.html
14. Statistical Abstract of the U.S.:
    http://www.census.gov/prod/www/statistical-abstract-us.html
15. Basic US Census Data Tables:
    http://www.oseda.missouri.edu/usinfo.html
16. The Gallup Organization: http://www.gallup.com/
17. CIA World Fact Book:
    http://www.odci.gov/cia/publications/factbook/index.html
18. Social Statistics Briefing Room:
    http://www.whitehouse.gov/fsbr/demography.html
19. Population Reference Bureau: http://www.prb.org/
20. U.S. Demography Homepage: http://www.ciesin.org/datasets/us-
    demog/us-demog-home.html
21. Population Index on the Web: http://popindex.princeton.edu/index.html
22. The Internet Guide to Demography and Population Studies:
    http://demography.anu.edu.au/VirtualLibrary/

23. Development, Social Transformation and Globalisation:
    http://www.uow.edu.au/research/groups/capstrans/pubs/castles.pdf
24. World Social Situation:
    http://caster.ssw.upenn.edu/~restes/praxis/world3.html

Modernization, Technology and Social Change

In order to get a handle on these issues you should read a piece by Peter Drucker written in 1994 and published in the Atlantic Monthly. You can access the paper at The Age of Social Transformation[25]. The Research About Social Change[26] web site is compiled and managed by Gene Shackman, Ph.D. and will help you to look at long term, large scale changes in social, political and economic systems at the national and international levels. The principal aim of the site is to present information that can be used to explain historical change, growth and development. For example: why did industrialization first occur in Europe; and what is globalization and how is it happening? The Internet Modern History Sourcebook contains a Summary of Wallerstein's World Systems Theory.[27] The Sourcebook is a collection of public domain and copy-permitted texts for introductory level classes in modern European and World history. This is an important document to include in any study of modernization. Professor Mauro Guillen's Globalization Literature Review[28] can be accessed from his page at the Wharton Faculty Research Website. From this site you can approach answering such questions as "Is Globalization Civilizing, Destructive or Feeble?" You will also find "A Critique of Five Key Debates in the Social Science Literature."

Information Technology and Citizen Participation,[29] is an indexed text of a paper presented David C. Neice of the Department of Canadian Heritage. It's a solid introduction to the subject. Good additional reading for a course on the dehumanizing aspects of technology. As an example of the many ways that social institutions are responding to modernization, technology and social change to the web site of Leonard Sweet[30] who is a professor of evangelism at Drew University. This is a website that addresses social change in the culture while providing methodologies for mainline Protestantism to reform its approach to ministry. There are a number of links, resources, articles, books, and a theology of social change. This is an excellent example of some of the effects of modernization and technology applied to religion.

Web Links

1. The Age of Social Transformation:
http://www.theatlantic.com/politics/ecbig/soctrans.htm

2. Research About Social Change:
http://redrival.net/evaluation/socialchange/research.html

3. Summary of Wallerstein's World Systems Theory:
http://www.fordham.edu/halsall/mod/wallerstein.html

4. Globalization Literature Review:
http://www-management.wharton.upenn.edu/guillen/

5. Information Technology and Citizen Participation:
http://www.fis.utoronto.ca/research/iprp/ua/neice.html

6. Leonard Sweet: www.leonardsweet.com

Careers in Sociology

Part of your research activity may be oriented toward your career. When you want to learn more about careers in sociology take this little tour:

1. Visit the web page of the American Sociological Association www.asanet.org[1] where you'll find one of the best examples of what professional sociology is all about. Go to the section created for students and then link to the page focusing primarily on careers in the field. Here you will find a number of important articles and profiles of positions in a number of fields in the discipline.

2. Your next step is to go to the Sociology Site[2] sponsored by Waycross College. This is a short list of World Wide Web resources for people interested in careers in sociology. Many of these pages are filled with links to job-hunting sites, sociology texts and papers, and sociological organizations.

3. For a good text on the subject of careers go to this site sponsored by Allyn and Bacon publishers. The entire text of Careers in Sociology[3] by W. Richard Stephens, Jr. is accessible chapter by chapter.

4. Now, you're ready to start looking at the market. The WWW Virtual Library[4] has a page that will link you to a vast number of sociology departments throughout the country.

Web Links

1. American Sociological Association: www.asanet.org
2. Sociology Site: http://www.way.peachnet.edu/library/sociology.htm
3. Careers In Sociology: http://www.abacon.com/socsite/careers.html
4. The WWW Virtual Library:
   http://www.princeton.edu:80/~sociolog/us_links.html

Conclusion

The Internet has opened up seemingly unlimited access to information and data. The real challenge for researchers is to find ways to transform this wealth of information into knowledge. The ever present temptation is to "shallow down" what we know. Increasing the variety of data does not in itself guarantee new depths of knowing. Students are using an ever-widening variety of information – initially it looks impressive. But careful examination often demonstrates a serious lack of understanding. Using the Internet to foster research should ultimately produce deeper knowledge. When it does not, then we are not using it – it is using us. The Internet cannot do the real work of research for us. This new technology marvelously enables researchers to find and retrieve greater amounts of data. But like all research, some is more meaningful than others. When we increase the amount of data we access we need to also enhance our abilities to discriminate as to its usefulness. I hope that this guide helps you to deepen your search for knowledge.

Web Links Address Glossary

Frequently Asked Questions

1. Netscape Communicator: http://homenetscape.com/browser/index.html
2. Internet Explorer: http://wwwmicrosof.com/windows/ie/
3. Acrobat Reader: http://adobe.com/prodindex/acrobat/readstep.html
4. Windows Media Player:
   http://www.microsoft.com/windows/mediaplayer/default.asp
5. RealJukebox: http://www.real.com/product/realjukebox/
6. RealPlayer: http://www.real.com/products/player
7. Quick Time: http://www.apple.com/quicktime/
8. Internet Detective: http://sosig.ac.uk/desire/internet-detective.html
9. Critical Thinking Resources:
   http://www.kcmetro.cc.mo.us/longview/ctac/toc.htm
10. A Student's Guide to WWW Research: Web Searching, Web Page EvaluationMSN.COM: http://home.microsoft.com/
11. Yahoo!: http://www.yahoo.com/
12. Netcenter: http://www.home.netscape.com/
13. The Sociological Tour Through Cyberspace
    http://www.trinity.edu/mkearl/index.html
14. The SocioWeb
    http://www.socioweb.com/~markbl/socioweb/
15. World Wide Web Virtual Library: Sociology
    http://www.mcmaster.ca/socscidocs/w3virtsoclib/index.htm
16. Data on the Net: http://odwin.ucsd.edu/idata/
17. About.com: http://www.about.com/
18. Sociology: http://sociology.about.com/science/sociology/mbody.htm
19. Virtual Society:The Wadsworth Sociology Resource Center
    http://sociology.wadsworth.com/
20. Welcome to WebRing!: http://www.webring.com/
21. Sociology Forum Web Ring:
    http://nav.webring.yahoo.com/hub?ring=socforum&list
22. The Sociology Ring:
    http://nav.webring.yahoo.com/hub?ring=sociology&list
23. World Wide Sociology Web Ring:
    http://nav.webring.yahoo.com/hub?ring=wwsociology&list
24. Everything Postmodern Web Ring:
    http://nav.webring.yahoo.com/hub?ring=epostmodern&list

25. Cyberstudies Web Ring: http://nav.webring.yahoo.com/hub?ring=cyberstudies&lis

Communicating

1. Netiquette Home Page: http://www.fau.edu/netiquette/netiquette.html
2. Lizst: http://www.liszt.com
3. Symantech's Anti Virus Reference Center: http://www.symantec.com/avcenter/index.html
4. Computer Incident Advisory Capability: http://ciac.llnl.gov/ciac/CIACHome.html
5. Urban Legends Archive: http://www.urbanlegends.com/
6. Urban Legends Reference Page: http://www.snopes.com/
7. DejaNews: http://www.deja.com/usenet/
8. Yahoo! Chat: http://chat.yahoo.com/
9. MSNBC Chat: http://www.msnbc.com/chat/default.asp
10. Internet Relay Chat (IRC) Help: http://www.irchelp.org/
11. Chat Etiquette/Chat Protocol: http://www.minopher.net.au/WebEd/protocol.htm
12. ICQ: http://www.icq.com/
13. AOL Instant Messenger: http://www.aol.com/aim/

Simple Searches

1. Yahoo!: http://www.yahoo.com/
2. UniGuide Academic Guide to the Internet: http://www.aldea.com/guides/ag/attframes2.html
3. StudyWeb: http://www.studyweb.com/
4. World Wide Web Virtual Library: http://www.vlib.org/
5. Argus Clearinghouse: http://www.clearinghouse.net/
6. WCSU List: Sociology Internet Resources: http://www.ahs.cqu.edu.au/psysoc/soconline/html/onlinres.htm
7. World Wide Web Virtual Library: Sociology: http://www.mcmaster.ca/socscidocs/w3virtsoclib/index.htm
8. SocioSite: http://www.pscw.uva.nl/sociosite/index.html
9. Encyclopedia Britannica: http://www.britannica.com/
10. My Virtual Reference Desk: http://www.refdesk.com/
11. Martindale's 'The Reference Desk': http://www-sci.lib.uci.edu/HSG/Ref.html
12. Information Please Almanac: http://www.infoplease.com/index.html
13. Infonation: http://www.un.org/Pubs/CyberSchoolBus/infonation/e_infonation.htm
14. World Encyclopedia: http://www.emulateme.com/
15. Map Machine: http://www.nationalgeographic.com/resources/ngo/maps/

16. Dead Sociologists Index: http://raven.jmu.edu/~ridenelr/DSS/INDEX.HTML
17. Biography.com: http://www.biography.com/
18. Ethnographic Atlas: http://lucy.ukc.ac.uk/EthnoAtlas/ethno.html
19. CIA World Factbook: http://www.odci.gov/cia/publications/factbook/index.html
20. Country Studies Series: http://lcweb2.loc.gov/frd/cs/cshome.html
21. Statistical Abstract of the U.S.: http://www.census.gov/statab/www/
22. Altavista: http://altavista.digital.com/
23. Fast Search: http://www.alltheweb.com/
24. Brightgate: http://www.brightgate.com/
25. NorthernLight: http://www.northernlight.co

Research on the Web

1. Academic Libraries:
   http://www.yahoo.com/Reference/Libraries/Academic_Libraries/
2. LibWeb: http://sunsite.berkeley.edu/Libweb/
3. Amazon.com: http://www.amazon.com/
4. abebooks.com: http://www.abebooks.com/
5. Bibliofind: http://www.bibliofind.com/
6. Internet Public Library: http://www.ipl.org/
7. The Online Books Page: http://www.cs.cmu.edu/books.html
8. Making of America: http://www.umdl.umich.edu/moa/
9. UnCover: http://uncweb.carl.org/
10. NorthernLight: http://www.northernlight.com/
11. Sociological Research Online: http://www.socresonline.org.uk/
12. The University of Chicago Press: http://www.journals.uchicago.edu/
13. How to Write Term Papers:
    http://www.dushkin.com/online/study/dgen2.mhtml
14. *The Elements of Style*: http://www.bartleby.com/141/index.html
15. Grammar Handbook:
    http://www.english.uiuc.edu/cws/wworkshop/grammarmenu.htm
16. On-Line English Grammar: http://www.edunet.com/english/grammar/index.html
17. Sources: Their Use and Acknowledgment:
    http://www.dartmouth.edu/~sources/index.html
18. MLA Style: http://www.mla.org/style/sources.htm
19. Electronic Reference Formats: http://www.apa.org/journals/webref.html
20. Fair Use of Copyrighted Works: http://www.cetus.org/fairindex.html
21. U.S. Copyright Office, FAQ: http://lcweb.loc.gov/copyright/faq.html

Current Events

1. ABC News: http://www.abcnews.com/
2. BBC News: http://news.bbc.co.uk/default.htm
3. The New York Times: http://www.nytimes.com/
4. US Newspaper Links: http://www.usnewspaperlinks.com/
5. SocioNews: http://www.sociologyonline.f9.co.uk/Socionews.htm
6. Artigen: http://www.artigen.com/
7. NewsHub: http://www.newshub.com/
8. NewsTracker : http://nt.excite.com/
9. TotalNews: http://www.totalnews.com/

Learning

1. Internet Guide & Web Tutorial:
   http://www.microsoft.com/insider/internet/default.htm
2. Webmonkey: A How To Guide for Web Developers:
   http://www.hotwired.com/webmonkey/
3. Sociology Online: http://www.sociologyonline.f9.co.uk/Home4NN.htm
4. Free-Ed.net: http://www.free-ed.net/fr09/fr0907.htm
5. What is Culture?:
   http://www.wsu.edu:8001/vcwsu/commons/topics/culture/culture-index.html
6. World Lecture Hall: http://www.utexas.edu/world/lecture/
7. Western Governors University: http://www.wgu.edu/
8. Southern Regional Electronic Campus: http://www.srec.sreb.org/
9. Committee on Institutional Cooperation: Common Market of Courses and Institutions: http://www.cic.uiuc.edu/CMCI/cmci_homepage.htm
10. Community College Distance Learning Network:
    http://ccdln.rio.maricopa.edu/

The Study of Society

1. Tour Through Cyber Society: http://www.trinity.edu/mkearl/index.html
2. Social Science Hub: http://www2.dynamite.com.au/kiwisunf/ss.htm
3. Sociology Web Hog: http://rock.uwc.edu/~pgroth/sochawg.htm

Sociological Theory

1. The Dead Sociologist's Society:
   http://raven.jmu.edu/~ridenelr/DSS/DEADSOC.HTML
2. Sociology Online: http://www.sociologyonline.co.uk/Home4NN.htm
3. SocioSite: http://www.pscw.uva.nl/sociosite/topics/sociologists.html
4. Sociology Café:
   http://www.geocities.com/Athens/Olympus/2147/basetheory.html

5. Classical Sociological Theory:
   http://www.spc.uchicago.edu/ssr1/PRELIMS/theory.html
6. The Voice of the Shuttle:
   http://vos.ucsb.edu/shuttle/cultural.html#authors
7. The Marxists Internet Archive:
   http://csf.colorado.edu/mirrors/marxists.org/
8. The Marxism Page: http://www.anu.edu.au/polsci/marx/marx.html
9. George's Page: http://paradigm.soci.brocku.ca/~lward/default.html
10. The Looking Glass Self:
    http://raven.jmu.edu/~ridenelr/courses/LKGLSSLF.HTML
11. The Durkheim Pages: http://www.lang.uiuc.edu/durkheim/
12. Michel Foucault: http://www.synaptic.bc.ca/ejournal/foucault.htm
13. Power and Bureaucracy:
    http://sol.brunel.ac.uk/~jarvis/bola/power/bureau.html
14. The Protestant Ethic and the Spirit of Capitalism: http://www.asahi-net.or.jp/~hw8m-mrkm/weber/world/ethic/pro_eth_frame.html
15. Verstehen:Max Weber's Webpage:
    http://msumusik.mursuky.edu/~felwell/http/weber/whome.htm
16. SocioRealm: http://www.geocities.com/CollegePark/Quad/5889/
17. Society for the Study of Symbolic Interactionism:
    http://sun.soci.niu.edu/~sssi/
18. Structural Functionalism and Parsons:
    http://uregina.ca/~gingrich/n2f99.htm
19. Functionalism: http://www.as.ua.edu/ant/Faculty/murphy/function.htm
20. World Socialist Web: http://www.wsws.org/
21. Cultural Logic: http://eserver.org/clogic/
22. Spoon Homepage: http://lists.village.virginia.edu/~spoons/

Research Methods

1. Research Methods Tutorials:
   http://trochim.human.cornell.edu/tutorial/TUTORIAL.HTM
2. Methods and Measurements:
   http://csbs.utsa.edu/social&policy/soc/masters/meth_meas.html
3. StatPages.net: http://members.aol.com/johnp71/javastat.html
4. Basic Statistics: www.robertniles.com
5. Bill Trochim's Center for Social Research Methods:
   http://trochim.human.cornell.edu/index.html
6. UCLA Statistics Textbook: http://home.stat.ucla.edu/textbook/
7. Social Research Update: http://www.soc.surrey.ac.uk/sru/Sru.html

8. A Student's Guide to Referencing On-line Information Sources in the Social Sciences: http://cua6.csuohio.edu/~ernie/courses/cite.htm

9. Guide for Citing Electronic Information: http://www.wpunj.edu/wpcpages/library/citing.htm

10. The Social Science Paper Publisher: http://www.sspp.net/

11. American Sociological Association's Style Guidelines and Manuscript Preparation Checklist: asanet.org/pubs/notice.pdf

12. SocioSite: http://www.pscw.uva.nl/sociosite/index.html

13. A Sociological Tour Through Cyberspace: http://www.trinity.edu/mkearl/index.html

14. The Dead Sociologist's Society: http://raven.jmu.edu/~ridenelr/DSS/DEADSOC.HTML

15. National Opinion Research Center: http://www.norc.uchicago.edu/

16. Gallup Research Center: http://www.unl.edu/unl-grc/

17. Indiana University at Bloomington: http://www.iub.edu/academic/centers.html

18. Institute for Public Opinion Research: http://www.fiu.edu/orgs/ipor/

19. The Survey Research Center at Princeton: http://www.princeton.edu/~abelson/

20. Survey Research Center: http://www.isr.umich.edu/src/

21. The National Science Foundation (Social, Behavioral and Economic Research): www.nsf.gov/sbe/redirect.htm

22. The Inter-University Consortium for Political and Social Research: www.icpsr.umich.edu/

23. National Archives and Records Administration Center for Electronic Records: www.nara.gov/nara/electronic/

24. Census Bureau: www.census.gov/

25. Federal Statistics: www.fedstats.gov/

26. World Database of Happiness: www.eur.nl/fsw/research/happiness/

Culture

1. Sociological Research Online: http://www.socresonline.org.uk/

2. World Lecture Hall: Sociology: http://www.utexas.edu/world/lecture/soc/

3. Britannica.com: http://search.britannica.com/search?query=culture

4. What is Culture?: http://carla.acad.umn.edu/culture.html

5. What is Culture: http://www.wsu.edu:8001/vcwsu/commons/topics/culture/culture-index.html

6. CIA World Fact Book: http://www.odci.gov/cia/publications/factbook/index.html

7. The Library of Congress Country Studies:
   http://lcweb2.loc.gov/frd/cs/cshome.html
8. A Sociology Guy's Anthropology Links:
   http://www.trinity.edu/~mkearl/anthro.html
9. Kinship and Social Organization:
   http://www.umanitoba.ca/anthropology/tutor/
10. The Ancient World Web: http://www.julen.net/ancient/
11. Washington State University World Civilizations:
    http://www.wsu.edu:8000/~dee/
12. About.com Culture Index:
    http://home.about.com/culture/index.htm?PM=59_0216_T
13. Multicultural Homepage:
    http://pasture.ecn.purdue.edu/~agenhtml/agenmc/
14. Multicultural Pavilion: http://curry.edschool.virginia.edu/go/multicultural/
15. popcultures.com: http://www.popcultures.com/
16. Cultural Studies Central: http://www.culturalstudies.net/
17. Center for the Study of Popular Culture: www.cspc.org
18. History of Cinema and Pop Culture:
    http://www.ex.ac.uk/bill.douglas/menu.html
19. Elvis Spotter's Website:
    http://fs.dai.net/ac/616480/N03.html?http://www.seanmccormick.com/
    Elvis

Organizations

1. Formal Organizations:
   http://www.src.uchicago.edu/ssr1/PRELIMS/orgs.htm
2. Historical Background of Organizational Behavior:
   http://www.cba.neu.edu/~ewertheim/introd/history.htm#Theoryx
3. History of the Discipline: http://www.cso.edu/memoire_a.htm
4. Complexity, Complex Systems & Chaos Theory, Organizations as Self-
   Adaptive Complex Systems: http://www.brint.com/Systems.htm
5. Learning Organization:
   www.newgrange.com/dfoffice/learning_organization.htm
6. Learning Organization Resources on the Web and on the Net:
   http://www.gpsi.com/lo.html
7. Society for Organizational Learning: http://www.sol-ne.org/

Economy

1. Department of Labor: http://www.dol.gov/
2. Bureau of Labor Statistics: http://stats.bls.gov/

3. Department of Labor National Longitudinal Surveys: http://stats.bls.gov/nlshome.htm

4. Federal Statistics: http://www.fedstats.gov/

5. National Bureau of Economic Research: http://www.nber.org/data_index.html

6. Panel Study of Income Dynamics: http://www.isr.umich.edu/src/psid/index.html

7. Economic Research and Data: http://woodrow.mpls.frb.fed.us/economy/

8. History of Economic Thought Website: http://cepa.newschool.edu/het/

Education

1. Department of Education: http://www.ed.gov/

2. Education World: http://www.education-world.com/

3. National Center for Education Statistics: http://nces.ed.gov/pubsearch/

4. Social Statistics Briefing Room: http://www.whitehouse.gov/fsbr/education.html

5. Michigan State University Educational Statistics: http://www.lib.msu.edu/corby/education/stat.htm

6. Higher Education Statistics Agency: http://www.hesa.ac.uk/

7. World Data on Education: http://www.ibe.unesco.org/Inf_Doc/Nat_reps/wdepfome.htm

Politics

1. Republican National Committee: www.RNC.com

2. Democratic National Committee: www.DNC.com

3. Government News Network: http://www.govnews.org/

4. Online Publications: http://osiris.colorado.edu/POLSCI/RES/pubs.html

5. Centre for Research into Elections and Social Trends: www.ox.ac.uk/

6. Harvard-MIT Data Center: http://hdc-www.harvard.edu/hdc/

7. Social Research Center: http://wwwspc.uchicago.edu/DATALIB/datalib.cgi?DIsearch/index

8. The Urban Institute: http://www.urban.org/

9. Evolutionary World Politics Homepage: http://faculty.washington.edu/modelski/

10. Teaching Resources: http://socsci.Colorado.EDU/POLSCI/RES/teaching.html#s

Marriage and Family

1. US Census Marital Status and Living Arrangements: http://www.census.gov/population/www/pop-profile/msla.html

2. US Census Households By Type:
    http://www.bls.census.gov/cps/pub/1997/hhldtype.htm
3. The Emerging 21st Century American Family:
    http://www.norc.uchicago.edu/online/emerge.pdf
4. Legal and Economic Benefits of Marriage:
    http://www.religioustolerance.org/mar_bene.htm
5. Family Sociology Resources:
    http://socsci.Colorado.EDU/SOC/RES/family.html
6. Family.com: http://family.go.com/
7. Kids Count Data and Publications:
    http://www.aecf.org/kidscount/index.htm
8. Family Resources on the Web:
    http://web.gc.cuny.edu/dept/socio/resource/family/index.htm
9. Australian Institute of Family Studies: http://www.aifs.org.au/
10. Resources on Domestic Violence:
    http://www.silcom.com/~paladin/madv/astrid.html
11. Cybergrrl Safety Net:
    http://www.cybergrrl.com/fs.jhtml?/views/dv/index.shtml
12. Strong Families Network: www.heavenbound.net/families/
13. Pure Love Alliance: http://purelove.org/top/who.html
14. Administration for Children and Families: http://www.acf.dhhs.gov/
15. State Child Support Enforcement Web Site:
    http://www.acf.dhhs.gov/programs/cse/extinf.htm
16. Research Forum on Children, Families, and the New Federalism:
    http://www.researchforum.org/
17. The Future of Children: http://www.futureofchildren.org/
18. State of the World's Children:
    www.unicef.org/sowc96/contents.htm?477,233
19. Family Relations:
    http://www.personal.psu.edu/faculty/n/x/nxd10/family3.htm
20. Marriage and Family Processes:
    http://www.trinity.edu/~mkearl/family.html
21. Human Development & Family Life Education Resource Center
    www.hec.ohio-state.edu/famlife/index.htm

Healthcare

1. Harris County Hospital District: http://www.tmc.edu/hchd/HCHD.html
2. Centers for Disease Control and Prevention: http://www.cdc.gov/
3. National Institutes of Health: http://www1.od.nih.gov/obssr/def.htm
4. Greenbook: http://aspe.os.dhhs.gov/98gb/toc.htm

5. The Combined Health Information Database: http://chid.nih.gov/

6. Dartmouth Atlas of Healthcare: http://www.dartmouthatlas.org/

7. Global Health Network: http://www.pitt.edu/HOME/GHNet/GHNet.html

Religion

1. American Religion Data Archive: http://www.arda.tm/

2. 1997 Yearbook of American & Canadian Churches: http://www.dnaco.net/~kbedell/ybstats2.htm

3. American Studies Web: http://www.georgetown.edu/crossroads/asw/philos.html

4. Religious Movements Homepage: http://cti.itc.virginia.edu/~jkh8x/soc257/

5. National Science Foundation: Religion, Democratization, and Market Transition Workshop: http://www.nsf.gov/sbe/ses/sociol/works3.htm

6. Max Weber's Sociology of Religion: http://4sociology.4anything.com/network-frame/0,1855,6401-62110,00.html

7. The American Religious Experience: http://are.as.wvu.edu/

8. Princeton University Center for the Study of Religion: http://www.princeton.edu/~csrelig/

9. Institute for the Study of American Religion: http://www.americanreligion.org/index.html

10. Apologetics Index: http://www.gospelcom.net/apologeticsindex/

11. Lectures on Southern Religion: http://www.wfu.edu:/~matthetl/south/lectures.html

12. Televangelism: http://cti.itc.virginia.edu/~jkh8x/tvrel/tvrelhome.htm

13. New Advent: Catholic Resources Online: http://www.newadvent.org/

14. www.Zipple.com

15. Jewish Online Student Research Center: http://www.us-israel.org/jsource/

16. The Islam World Net: http://www.islamworld.net/

17. Native American Spirituality: http://cti.itc.virginia.edu/~jkh8x/soc257/nrms/naspirit.html

18. The Church of Jesus Christ of Latter Day Saints: http://www.lds.org/

19. The Book of Mormon (online): http://www.hti.umich.edu/m/mormon//browse.html

20. New Religious Movements: http://www.academicinfo.net/nrms.html

21. Links to Revelation, Apocalyptic and Millennial Websites and Materials: http://clawww.lmu.edu/faculty/fjust/Apocalyptic_Links.htm

Gender and Women's Studies

1. Women's and Gender Studies Database on the Internet :
   http://www.uni-koeln.de/phil-fak/englisch/datenbank/e_index.htm
2. UN Internet Gateway for Women's Studies :www.un.org/womenwatch
3. Women's Studies/Resources Research Sites:
   http://www.unix.umbc.edu/~korenman/wmst/links.html
4. Feminism and Women's Studies:
   http://eserver.org/feminism/index.html
5. American Studies Web:
   http://www.georgetown.edu/crossroads/asw/wmst.html
6. Feminist Theory Website :www.cddc.vt.edu/feminism/
7. Gender and Society: http://www.trinity.edu/mkearl/gender.html
8. Jane Addams Biography and Quotes:
   http://4sociology.4anything.com/network-frame/0,1855,6401-
   61283,00.html
9. Women in Politics Database :http://www.ipu.org/bdf-e/BDFsearch.asp
10. Feminist Majority Foundation Online:www.feminist.org
11. Feminism and Women's Resources:
    http://www3.50megs.com/jmansfield//feminism/index.html
12. American Men's Studies Association:
    http://members.aol.com/amsapage/
13. Menstuff National Mens Resource:http://www.menstuff.org/
14. Earning Differences Between Men and Women:
    http://www.dol.gov/dol/wb/public/wb_pubs/wagegap2.htm

Social Class

1. U.S. Census Bureau Income Statistics:
   http://www.census.gov/ftp/pub/hhes/www/income.html
2. U.S. Census Bureau Poverty Statistics:
   http://www.census.gov/ftp/pub/hhes/www/poverty.html
3. 1998 Greenbook: http://aspe.os.dhhs.gov/98gb/toc.htm
4. Explorations in social inequality http://www.trinity.edu/mkearl/strat.html
5. Why the Poor are Poor: http://www.trinity.edu/mkearl/socpsy-8.html#wp
6. Inequality.org: http://www.inequality.org/
7. Lecturesonline.org:
   http://www.lecturesonline.org/social_sciences/sociology.htm
8. SocioSite's social inequality and stratification resources:
   http://www.pscw.uva.nl/sociosite/TOPICS/Inequality.html\

9. Harvard University's Inequality and Social Policy Web Site Think Tank Links:
http://www.ksg.harvard.edu/inequality/Focus/links.htm

10. American Heritage's ranking of the wealthiest American's of all time:
http://www.americanheritage.com/98/oct/40index.htm

11. Veblen's Theory of the Leisure Class:
http://socserv2.socsci.mcmaster.ca/~econ/ugcm/3ll3/veblen/leisure/index.html

12. National Coalition for the Homeless: http://nch.ari.net/

13. The Austin Chronicles Hypermedia Gallery on Homeless Teenagers:
http://www.auschron.com/gallery/

14. Homelessness in America:
http://www.qvctc.commnet.edu/student/GaryOKeefe/homeless/frame.html

Race And Ethnicity

1. Race and Ethnicity http://www.trinity.edu/mkearl/race.html

2. American Studies Web:
http://www.georgetown.edu/crossroads/asw/genethnic.html

3. African American Internet Links:
http://latino.sscnet.ucla.edu/Afro.links.html

4. Latino Internet Sites: http://latino.sscnet.ucla.edu/latinos.links.html

5. Asian American Sites: http://latino.sscnet.ucla.edu/Asian.links.html

6. Race and Ethnic Studies Institute: http://resi.tamu.edu/index.html

7. Virtual Library on Migration and Ethnic Relations:
http://www.ercomer.org/wwwvl/

8. The Race and Ethnicity Collection: http://eserver.org/race/

9. The Origins of Affirmative Action: http://www.now.org/nnt/08-95/affirmhs.html

10. The Arayan Nations Web Site: http://www.christian-aryannations.com/

11. African American Web Connection: http://www.aawc.com/aawc0.html

12. The Hoover Institute:
http://www-hoover.stanford.edu/publications/he/23/23a.html

13. About the Hoover Institution:
http://www-hoover.stanford.edu/main/whatis.html

Social Control And Deviance

1. National Archive for Criminal Justice Data:
http://www.icpsr.umich.edu/NACJD/

2. U.S. Dept of Justice, Bureau of Justice Statistics:
http://www.ojp.usdoj.gov/bjs/pubalp2.htm

3. Bureau of Justice Statistics Homepage:
http://www.ojp.usdoj.gov/bjs/welcome.html

4. Crime and Victims Statistics, Bureau of Justice Statistics:
   http://www.ojp.usdoj.gov/bjs/cvict.htm
5. Statistics on Drugs and Crime, Bureau of Justice Statistics:
   http://www.ojp.usdoj.gov/bjs/drugs.htm
6. Information Products from the Bureau of Justice Statistics
   Clearinghouse: http://www.ncjrs.org/statprdt.htm
7. International Justice Statistics, Bureau of Justice Statistics:
   http://www.ojp.usdoj.gov/bjs/ijs.htm
8. Social Statistics Briefing Room:
   http://www.whitehouse.gov/fsbr/crime.html
9. The DEA Homepage: http://www.usdoj.gov/dea/
10. The FBI Homepage: http://www.fbi.gov/homepage.htm
11. FBI Uniform Crime Reports: http://www.fbi.gov/ucr.htm
12. Federal Bureau of Prisons: http://www.bop.gov/fact0598.html
13. Federal Crime Statistics Organizational Index: http://www.crime.org/fed-index.html
14. National Criminal Justice Reference Service: http://www.ncjrs.org/
15. Criminal Justice Statistics: http://www.ncjrs.org/statwww.htm
16. Supreme Court Decisions: http://supct.law.cornell.edu:8080/supct/
17. Crime Mapping Research Center: http://www.ojp.usdoj.gov/cmrc/
18. Office of Juvenile Justice and Delinquency Prevention:
    http://ojjdp.ncjrs.org/
19. Sociology Online: Criminology
    http://www.sociologyonline.f9.co.uk/SubjectAreasNNCrime.htm
20. ACLU Criminal Justice Page:
    http://www.aclu.org:80/issues/criminal/hmcj.html

Social Movements, Demography and Globalization

1. ASA Section on Collective Behavior and Social Movements:
   http://www.u.arizona.edu/~jearl/cbsm.html
2. Social Activism Sites on the Web:
   http://www.u.arizona.edu/~jearl/active.htm
3. Narratives of Possibility: Social Movements, Collective Stories, and the
   Dilemmas of Practice: http://www.interweb-tech.com/nsmnet/docs/kling.htm
4. New Social Movement Network: http://www.interweb-tech.com/nsmnet/
5. Computer Linked Social Movements:
   http://www.eco.utexas.edu/faculty/Cleaver/polnet.html
6. Social Movement Cultures: http://www.wsu.edu:8080/~amerstu/smc/

7. SocioSite Special Forms of Activism and Social Movements:
   http://www.pscw.uva.nl/sociosite/TOPICS/Activism.html#SPECIAL

8. Latin American Social Movements on the WWW:
   http://www.ncl.ac.uk/library/guides/lasmig.html

9. Women and Social Movements in the United States:
   http://womhist.binghamton.edu/

10. Black/African Related Resources:
    http://www.sas.upenn.edu/African_Studies/Home_Page/mcgee.html

11. Collective Behavior and Social Movements:
    http://www.abacon.com/sociology/soclinks/collect.html

12. www.Cybersociology.com

13. Grassroots Political Activism Online:
    http://www.socio.demon.co.uk/magazine/5/issue5.html

14. Statistical Abstract of the U.S.:
    http://www.census.gov/prod/www/statistical-abstract-us.html

15. Basic US Census Data Tables:
    http://www.oseda.missouri.edu/usinfo.html

16. The Gallup Organization: http://www.gallup.com/

17. CIA World Fact Book:
    http://www.odci.gov/cia/publications/factbook/index.html

18. Social Statistics Briefing Room:
    http://www.whitehouse.gov/fsbr/demography.html

19. Population Reference Bureau: http://www.prb.org/

20. U.S. Demography Homepage: http://www.ciesin.org/datasets/us-demog/us-demog-home.html

21. Population Index on the Web: http://popindex.princeton.edu/index.html

22. The Internet Guide to Demography and Population Studies:
    http://demography.anu.edu.au/VirtualLibrary/

23. Development, Social Transformation and Globalisation:
    http://www.uow.edu.au/research/groups/capstrans/pubs/castles.pdf

24. World Social Situation:
    http://caster.ssw.upenn.edu/~restes/praxis/world3.html

Modernization, Technology and Social Change

1. The Age of Social Transformation:
   http://www.theatlantic.com/politics/ecbig/soctrans.htm

2. Research About Social Change:
   http://redrival.net/evaluation/socialchange/research.html

3. Summary of Wallerstein's World Systems Theory:
   http://www.fordham.edu/halsall/mod/wallerstein.html

4. Globalization Literature Review:
   http://www-management.wharton.upenn.edu/guillen/

5. Information Technology and Citizen Participation:
   http://www.fis.utoronto.ca/research/iprp/ua/neice.html

6. Leonard Sweet: www.leonardsweet.com

Careers In Sociology

1. American Sociological Association: www.asanet.org

2. Sociology Site: http://www.way.peachnet.edu/library/sociology.htm

3. Careers In Sociology: http://www.abacon.com/socsite/careers.html

4. The WWW Virtual Library:
   http://www.princeton.edu:80/~sociolog/us_links.html

GLOSSARY

Archie. A method of searching for programs on the Internet before the widespread availability of the web.

bandwidth. A measure of how fast data can be transmitted from one point to another in bits per second.

bookmark. A method of recording the address of a web site using your browser so that you can return to it without typing in the address.

browser. The software that interprets the formatting and programing codes that are contained in web pages. Browsers display web pages so that you can read them. They also transmit your commands back to the web site.

cookie. A small file on your computer that contains information that can be transmitted to a web site when you visit it. Cookies allow web sites to shop for products (they keep track of your shopping cart) and they allow you to customize web pages so that the content you want is there whenever you return.

domain name. Domain names are used to locate computers on the Internet. Minimally domain names consist of a name and a suffix. The suffix is usually .edu, .com, .net, .org, or .gov in the United States, but each country also has its own suffix (for example, the United Kingdom is .uk).
electronic bulletin board. Electronic bulletin boards allow visitors to post messages that can be read by others. The advantage of a bulletin board is that the messages are not distributed as email messages so they do not all end up in your mailbox whether you are interested in them or not. The disadvantage is that the messages drop off the board after a few days or weeks so that you can miss messages if you do not check the board regularly. The biggest collection of bulletin boards is **usenet** (see below).

Email. Short for electronic mail, email consists of text messages that are sent from one person to another person. The message waits at the recipient's mailbox until it is discarded by the recipient.

Frequently Asked Questions (faq). Frequently Asked Questions are collections of common questions and their answers that have been written by people all over the world. They are not limited to topics concerning the Internet or computers. Originally these documents were distributed by usenet, but now they typically reside on a web site. There are faqs on almost any topic you can imagine.

Gopher. A precursor of the **World Wide Web** (see below). Gopher distributed text files that could be displayed by software programs (called gopher clients). Image and sound files could also be retrieved, but were not combined into a single display. Gopher was well-suited to limited bandwidth and slower computers that did not display graphics.

hypertext. A document that includes text, images, and links which are combined into a single computer display by browsers. It is the basis of the World Wide Web.

Hypertext Markup Language (html). The language for describing hypertext documents so that the pieces can be retrieved and combined by the browser.

HyperText Transfer Protocol (http). The communication method used by computers to transfer hypertext documents from one computer (the server or host) to another (the client).

Internet. The Internet is global network of computer networks that connects different kinds of computers so that they can share information.

Internet Relay Chat (irc). A method of allowing several people to transmit text messages to one another over the Internet. The people who want to chat all link to a particular chat room.

instant messaging (im). A method of sending a message from one person to another as long as both computers are connected to the Internet and both are running compatible Instant messaging software.

mailbox. Every email address has a mailbox, a space on the hard disk drive of the computer that receives email messages. Email stays in the mailbox until it is retrieved or deleted. Most mailboxes have size limits (for example, 1 or 2 megabytes of email). When the limit is reached, incoming messages are returned to the sender.

mailing list. A mailing list consists of a group of people (subscribers) who wish to exchange email messages on a particular topic. Any message sent by one subscriber to the mailing list is distributed to all of the subscribers.

newsgroup. A newsgroup is a form of electronic bulletin board. usenet newsgroups are grouped into hierarchies that indicate the general topic of the group. For example, the groups that begin with "comp." are concerned with computing issues and the groups beginning with "sci." are concerned with the sciences.

newsreader. A newsreader is a software program that allows you to retrieve and post messages to newsgroups.

plug-ins. Plug-ins are software programs that work within your web browser to handle file types that the browser cannot interpret. For example, plug-ins handle files containing video, sound, and virtual worlds.

portal. A web site that provides access to many features on a single page. A portal usually contains a subject classification of the web and a web search box, as well as news, stock prices, weather, sports, and other information. Most portals can be customized so that you select what features are included.

spam. Spam is the email equivalent of junk mail. It is email that you have solicited and that usually involves some kind of advertising.

start page. The web page that your browser loads when you first start it up. The default page is set by the company that distributes the browser, but you can change it to any other web page. You can also create a simple web page on your computer and use that as the start page.

virus. A computer program that copies itself to other computers. Just like biological viruses, software viruses can be relatively benign or they can destroy data on your computer. They are carried in software programs and document files. Virus protection software is generally effective, but you should still keep current backup copies of all of your important files.

web rings. A group of web sites that provide links to one another so that you can easily jump from one to another.

World Wide Web (www). Much of the information on the Internet is now organized through html documents and hyperlinks that allow you to combine text from one site with an image from another site with sound from a third site. This ability to link resources around the world is the World Wide Web.

Universal Resource Locator (url). An url is the address of a file on the World Wide Web. It allows the browser to select it out of all the files that are accessible on the web.

usenet. The USEr NETwork is the hierarchical collection of newsgroups including "comp.", "alt.", "sci.", "talk.", and others.